Have Mercy

Have Mercy

A Nursing Memoir

Mary Herbst

Maureen Ott

Maureen Weber

BOOKLOGIX®
Alpharetta, Georgia

ISBN: 978-1-61005-348-8

Printed in the United States of America

∞This paper meets the requirements of ANSI/NISO Z39.48-1992 (Permanence of Paper)

This is a work of nonfiction. It also is a work of creative remembrance, as we tried our best to recall details, events and happenings of three years of nursing school in the 1960s. With no intention to harm anyone or anything, we have tried to tell our story. Due to the passage of time and the loss of some grey matter, our memories may be missing elusive details. In writing this book, we have included three varying perspectives of a shared story. The truth, as we recall it, remains as each of us remembers it. If any Mercy Girls have a different version of the Mercy years, we invite them to write the sequel.

Cover Art/Design: Charles-Philippe Girard from alphaboy.com
Cover Image of Nuns: Alice Duc Triano, Queenston, Ontario
Author Photo: Beth Foster

For student nurses everywhere: know that you have a shared history with all nurses always.

To Sister Mary Claver, (our beloved "Beaver"). We have always remembered your instructions: "Get in! Get out and distract the patient!"

And for the "Mercy Girls," our nursing school colleagues, who have given us such joy, caring and enduring friendship.

"We write to taste life twice, in the moment and in retrospect."

–Anaïs Nin

Contents

Section 4:
Back To the Future

Preface

How Three Nurses Became Three Authors

We still talk about it...our nursing student days and years at Mercy Hospital. It was 1960. America had a Catholic president in the White House and everything seemed possible. We were committed to being nursing students for three years. It changed us in ways we could not have imagined. It's almost fifty years later, and the "Mercy Girls" still talk about our lives at Mercy.

The culture of nursing schools in the 60s was such a unique living and working (i.e., controlled) environment that eventually we came to believe that there was a story waiting and worth telling.

The first, but not last, idea for our book came about on a late summer evening in July 2008 at Maureen (Moe) Weber's home in Lewiston, a tiny village on the Niagara River in Western New York.

Gale-force winds were blowing story ideas our way, and as usual, we could not resist reliving nursing school days. We were looking forward to our forty-fifth nursing school reunion to be held that fall in Niagara Falls.

As always, we imagined the improbable scenario of today's nursing students trying to survive our student world back then— with only one public pay phone on each floor, or housemothers doing a bedtime check with a blazing flashlight in the face; unbelievable! But we thought nothing of it at the time.

We decided that night that we should write a book, and our brains tumbled into excited overdrive, like a car without brakes plunging down a hill.

And so, the idea was born...all that remained was to write it down and send it on its way.

We decided to keep our book a secret. We wanted to surprise the rest of the Mercy Girls, and planned to publish in time for our fiftieth nursing reunion in 2013. Our nursing friends could easily have become suspicious, however, as we peppered them with questions during the following months as we searched for "memory ammunition" for the book.

And that's how the story came about...three Mercy Girls deciding to become "rememberers" (is that a word?) and "documenters" of their nursing school years.

Today, we have changed, but we have not changed. We slip into conversation with each other now as easily as we did years ago. There were sixty-six student nurses when it all began on September 6, 1960, and more than fifty remain today. Most classmates still stay in touch with each other, something we think of as special and unusual, and something of which we like to boast.

Many of us would agree that it is our friendships that help keep us sane and alive. Then as always, the Mercy Girls have shared good times and bad, with a hug and with love for each other—a gift, to be sure, for us all.

Stephen King has said that everybody has a history and that most of it isn't even interesting. He counsels writers to stick to the good parts and ignore the rest. We hope we have followed his good advice.

This is a shared story—a story about personal growth, struggles and survival in a new environment and new career. It is also a story of laughter, foibles, and what it meant to be a student nurse in the 1960s.

Mary tells her story with a dry wit, Moe's stories have incredible photographic recall, and Mumme has...well...*experiences* to share. Most of us are now retired from our long-cherished nursing careers. We think it is time for a rest and for other things. We think it is time for the story to be told...*Have Mercy*!

Acknowledgments

Many people helped us in so many ways. How grateful we are to all the Mercy Girls who willingly gave us tidbits of their stories and essential school memorabilia—and helped us sort out the flotsam and jetsam of memories.

Deep thanks to Charles-Philippe Girard from alphaboy.com (Cover Designer) for his expertise in digital design, online collaboration workflows, and creative vision.

With gratitude to our editor, Bob Giannetti, of Bob's Olde Books in Lewiston, New York, who handled our wordy manuscript with great patience, always urging us to keep the "good parts" and edit the hell out of the rest.

We also thank Matthew Weber, for providing sound legal advice. He had a real knack for simplifying the complex, and unmuddling the muddled.

Introduction

The 1960s – Times of Transition and Turmoil

It was in 1960 that the Mercy Hospital School of Nursing Class of 1963 began the steps on the path to becoming nurses. We were part of a conflicted time that was marked by a culture of extremes. In our youth, the 1950s, television sitcoms had depicted a pristine family life where women were portrayed as family servants in spotless dresses with aprons and high-heeled shoes as they cooked and cleaned. In the meantime, Marilyn Monroe was an American icon that was in general, undressed.

The decade of the paranoia of McCarthyism, bomb shelters, the beginning of the nuclear buildup, and the Korean War had ended. Consumerism was increasing. The population had shifted from the cities to suburbia, which called for a car in every garage, and a highway system that allowed for easier access from urban to rural areas.

There were no childproof caps on bottles, no helmets for bike riding, and water came out of the garden hose rather than plastic bottles. Children played outside in the neighborhood, from morning to night and rushed home in packs to meet the parental dictum, "make sure that you are home before the streetlights come on." Computers were in the future. We were unaware of the term "globalization."

In 1960, John F. Kennedy became the President of the United States. He challenged Americans in his Inaugural Address to "Ask not what your country can do for you—ask what you can do for your country." John Kennedy's challenge brought some Americans to join the newly formed Peace Corps. Others became the conscience of a nation as they questioned the inequalities of racism and sexism.

The Cuban Missile Crisis made us feel vulnerable as we were informed that nuclear missiles in that nearby country were pointed in the direction of the United States. Many of us hurried to the confessional to purge our sins in case this was the beginning of the end. Space exploration helped us to turn heavenward but left us earthbound as we competed with the Russians for technological advancement in rocketry. The Vietnam War was starting to cast a long shadow on American history.

The Mercy Hospital Class of 1963 was protected from some of these events and immersed in others. The safety program at Mercy, in an all-out effort to protect the students from an atomic disaster, instructed "all students in case of an atomic disaster proceed as indicated on the floor plans to the ground floor and line up in two corridors near class rooms" (from page 18 of *The Handbook of Mercy Hospital School of Nursing*). We wonder if the author of this sentence stopped to consider how well this could have been coordinated. Maybe it was an attempt to do something, when in actuality, nothing could be done.

On a lighter note, bouffant hairstyles were considered "the rage" and were permitted. It was okay to have hair that was so large that it might cause flight patterns to change, but it better not touch your collar. The trend for shorter skirts was absent from our lives. As we were fitted for our uniforms, great care was taken to measure the distance from the hemline to the floor to make sure that no one would see any "suggestive" part of the leg above the ankle. Those same uniforms had enough starch to stand on their own without a body inside them. They were unyielding enough to cause a case of "redneck."

Birth Control pills allowed some to realize the possibility of sexual freedom, but not at Mercy where "gentlemen callers" were scrutinized and treated as possible sexual predators. In 1963, *The Feminine Mystique* by Betty Friedan was introduced. This book took a look at the society that created sexual inequality and the violation of women's rights instead of blaming the individual woman for her "lot in life." At Mercy, there was little "Mystique."

We had been taught in Catholic High Schools that sexual "sins" are the fault of the girl. If a girl were to become pregnant, she caused it because the boy couldn't help himself. It's in a man's nature. This is what was taught to the girls. We still wonder what theory of sexuality was taught to the guys.

We would personally transform ourselves during those three years, either despite our place in society or because of it.

Section 1

Mary Wintermantel Herbst

Do I think that the years of life after Mercy seemed to pass in a heartbeat? No, I do not! It wasn't hard to leave behind endless rules and restrictions, but it was difficult to find my place in nursing. I tried the clinical areas of Obstetrics, Pediatrics, Public Health, Psychiatry, Medical-Surgical Nursing, and returning to school for a BSN and an MS and found my calling in Critical Care. Fortunately, I did not try out husbands in the same manner and have been married to the same character since 1966. We enjoy our children, grandchildren and each other, even if his passion is hockey and mine is poetry.

Chapter One

Prologue

Memories

Memories are selective. Some are forever a part of who we are, etched within us, to be recalled at will. Others take on a new meaning with the passage of time. As we write about events that took place so many years ago, we admit that perfect recall is lost, as we have added more dimensions and encounters to our frames of reference.

In writing this memoir, we have represented our classmates through the experiences of several main characters. We chose this style of writing so the reader would not feel inundated with sixty-six separate characters to remember. If you can't find yourself or any specific characters from the class, look in Moe Weber's section. She never forgot anyone's escapades (or their former boyfriends).

Each member of The Mercy Hospital School Class of 1963 shares an important part of the story. Each had an integral role and each in their unique contributions has enhanced our experiences. We are grateful to have them in our lives. This is also their story—a story that began in 1960.

The Nursing Program at Mercy was based on the laws of absolute authority. Anything less would be cause for dismissal or confinement to the dormitory, which was called "being campused." In general, we started at Mercy as seventeen- or eighteen-year-old women who were living away from home for the first time and hoped to relish some newfound freedom.

However, fate intervened and parental authority looked lax compared to what the Mercy Handbook dictated. Some students found that the restrictions were stifling and looked for creative outlets to lighten the atmosphere. As we look back, we realize that the laughter enriched our lives and created a time of shared joy. Pleasurable and fun loving moments can be some of the best ways of enjoying these retreats into the past. It is with this purpose that we share our memoirs with you. But first a poem to show how we haven't changed:

Sexual Goddess

I see a woman in 4-inch heels and a short slinky
dress.
I think back in time, and I must confess, I never
was a
sexual goddess.

At 18, a uniform long enough to expose
white polished shoes and thick support hose.
Covered up completely in starched white bags
with a dress code just as rigid in rules and regs.
Hair off my collar, never expose an ear
where someone might whisper what a lady
should not hear.
Light lipstick for makeup, a watch to
accessorize,
fit beneath a uniform twice my size.

If I could go back, don 4 inch heels and a short
slinky
dress

I now confess, I would still be a nurse, not a
sexual
goddess.

Chapter Two

A Chartered Course
to an Unchartered Path

Decisions, Decisions, Decisions

Our senior year in high school, we were supposed to know what we wanted to do after graduation. I never considered nursing since I really, really wanted to be a woman detective who traveled around the world as an extraordinary crime fighter.

I felt I might pursue this career because, many times, I could guess who the murderer was before the end of a TV show. This seemed like significant criteria for success. However, there did not seem to be a lot of college courses at that time for my choice of professions.

The teachers I knew were almost all nuns who told us that we would hear the call if we had a religious vocation. No one ever called me. I went to a cottage on the shore of Lake Erie on the summer before senior year where my friend "Sis" said she had decided to be a nurse and had applied at Mercy Hospital School of Nursing. Her enthusiasm was contagious, and I thought to myself that I liked taking care of anyone who seemed ill and the school wasn't impossibly expensive. Also, it meant the freedom of living in a dorm, although not quite the life of a world famous crime investigator.

"Why do you want to be a nurse?" my mother asked. "You will be spending a lot of time with sick people." Although her words were not exactly a glowing endorsement of the nursing profession, she could not be faulted for their accuracy. She felt that the choice of careers after high school in the early 1960s for women included teaching, secretarial work, or nursing. I did not mention that I was thinking of becoming a detective. My mother had been a single secretary and had great fun living in Brooklyn until she joined the ranks of the married.

After seventeen years of studying my mother, I knew which points of a debate could secure a win. I pointed out that the school was only twenty miles from home and in an area where my mother had grown up. The cost was not exorbitant, it would provide a lifetime of meaningful employment, and I really liked "sick" people. My mother began to cave in but wondered why anyone with any sanity would prefer life among the ill.

Thus, the process of admission to Mercy Hospital School of Nursing began. After submitting an application, the next step was an interview with the infamous Sister Mary Ethel. I worried about passing Sister's in-depth scrutiny so I dressed for the occasion in clothes that would not reveal anything other than my head, hands and feet since this was the way that nuns dressed. It must be what they preferred to wear. My mother, who still questioned the wisdom of this decision, gathered her keys, purse, and rosary beads and we headed out the door to South Buffalo.

Path to the Future

The determination of road routes in Buffalo is often defined by water since you can't drive across a river or over a creek other than by a bridge. We drove from Kenmore, a suburb north of the city, along the Niagara River to the edge of Lake Erie. As we passed the downtown area, on the other side of the road away from the water, were grain mills, concrete factories, and railroads as evidence of the industrial nature of the landscape.

Our destiny eventually took us inland where I could see the silhouettes of the buildings of Bethlehem Steel in the distance. My mother informed me that the residents of this area, where she grew up, were proud of their South Buffalo heritage. It seemed to be a matter of pride to the natives of this area to distinguish themselves from the Northern, Western, and Eastern Buffalo sections. The homes were neat with manicured lawns and gardens.

We turned onto Abbott Road and immediately a carnivorous building with a sign "Mercy Hospital" came into view. It seemed to dwarf everything else in the neighborhood. It looked like a fortress to protect the nearby community. Behind this huge edifice was Marian Hall, which housed Mercy Hospital School of Nursing. We found Sister Mary Ethel in her office where she was ready and waiting.

The Interrogation

The interview process began with Sister sitting behind her desk and staring at this potential student to determine if "this one" was worthy of admission to "HER" school. Her deep-set brown eyes seemed to peer through me to search out my heart, mind, and soul. She sized me up from head to toe and asked if I was just coming to Mercy to attend Canisius College where there were ten males for every female student. (I wondered if she had failed to notice that I was dressed "somewhat" like a nun.) If so, she warned, "you had better think twice." On the last point, my mother, who was present at the interview, began to have hope that her daughter might be sane after all.

Sister Mary Ethel proceeded to warn of the rigors of nursing as well as the strict rules and regulations of the program. After a few weeks at the school, it became apparent that Sister Mary Ethel was right about the ratio at Canisius College, however she had skimped on the rules at Mercy, which would have been overly adequate for Alcatraz. Sister explained that this was a thirty-three month program, including summers, with a freshman, junior, and senior year. After her message about the rigorous program, I knew that I would never, ever miss that sophomore year. I wondered how many potential students sat through that initial interview with the same "deer in the headlights" look.

The Dorm

In order to start the three-year process of turning adolescent daydreamers into mature nurses, we began life in the Mercy dorm. The dorm building was located in the shadow of Mercy

Hospital, which should have been a warning of what was to come.

Upon entering the building, if you looked to the left, Sister Mary Ethel's office was positioned so she was able to perch on her chair to be continually observant for any infraction of the rules. After passing the required physical exam and Sister Mary Ethel's attempt to weed out the riff-raff, those who had managed to survive both of these vigilant processes became members of the Mercy Hospital School of Nursing Class of 1963.

In the winter, you could travel from the dorm to the hospital via an underground tunnel that was filled with pipes and unusual scary noises. Anyone who had watched any fright night shows or Alfred Hitchcock's movies could imagine all sorts of horrors in that tunnel, so they ran as quickly as possible to avoid any *Psycho*-type drama.

Chapter Three
Did I Enter the Convent?

Class Characters

Two students arrived from Niagara Falls, New York. One was Emilie N., who was sweet and innocent with the attitude that nuns can absolutely "do nothing wrong." The other was Maureen O. (nicknamed Moe), who was more worldly and had the opinion that nuns can "do nothing right." She was going to be a nurse and she would do whatever it took to achieve that goal.

Another Maureen, with the nickname Mumme, was in the class. I remembered her from high school as a quiet girl with a mischievous air about her. As time went by, her creative spirit and intelligence kept everyone laughing in the most trying of moments. We learned from her, the healing power of laughter. She spent a lot of time in Sister Mary Ethel's office. Maureen number three (there were five Maureens in the class) was nicknamed "Sis." She was sophisticated but also possessed the ability to find humor in the toughest times. In freshmen year, it was difficult to keep the Maureens straight, but with the passage of time their personalities defined them more than their names. Maureen R. and Cornelia looked the part of professional nurses from the first time they put on their uniforms and caps. I wanted to be like them, but as hard as I tried, I never managed it.

Yolanda was also a friend from high school. She would listen intently to the rules, ponder the situation, and was astute enough to determine whether or not they were worth following. One student arrived from Pennsylvania. She told us that she had chosen Mercy because she had heard that a hospital in the Buffalo area was named after a virtue and it had an excellent School of Nursing. Other students asked her if she had picked the wrong virtue and might have preferred charity as the Sisters of Charity had a hospital with a nursing school nearby. Probably chastity would have been the most likely virtue. We had little choice but to practice that one with all the restrictions.

Requirements, Rules and Restrictions

In early September 1960, the future nurses were called to a meeting where Sister Mary Ethel and her associates handed out the infamous *Blue Handbook of the Rules and Regulations of Mercy Hospital School of Nursing*. I remember wondering if students who could not read had been admitted to the program because the nuns proceeded to read the entire handbook to us. We would know that book well by the end of three years as it was quoted frequently. College students today, who live in coed dorms, might regard this way of life as part of "the dark ages" and they would be right.

During freshman year, we were to be studying at our desks in the dorm from Monday to Thursday from five p.m. to eight p.m. with a break for fifteen minutes at six-thirty p.m. No interruptions were permitted including phone calls or visiting each other. In case a student decided to test this policy, the Housemother would be performing random checks.

Students were to be in the dorm at ten-thirty p.m. every night and in bed by eleven o'clock. On weekends, you were allowed one midnight curfew. The Housemother would again act as the sheriff of the dorm.

> Students must be in the residence at 10:30 p.m. Lights out by 11:00 p.m. Students are to go to their own rooms at 10:30 p.m....Freshmen remaining in the nurse's residence during the week-end free time may obtain a 12:00 p.m. late leave on either Saturday or Sunday evening...Junior and Senior students have permission for two twelve o'clock leaves and one overnight, or two overnights weekly *(Student Handbook, Mercy Hospital School of Nursing)*.

I remember vividly the first night in the dorm like it was yesterday; lying in bed at about eleven and wondering if I might be bailed out of here because it sure felt like jail. I thought I had better stay for a week or two because my mother had spent hours sewing curtains to fit the windows in my dorm room. This might not seem like a valid reason for continuing to pursue a career, but my mother would not be amused. Another important consideration was that the first tuition had been paid in full.

Abruptly, the door was opened by a person carrying a flashlight. Every fright night show immediately came to mind as the hair on the back of my arms stood up straight. Stifling a blood-curdling scream, I asked the intruder, "Who are you?" She answered, "I am the Housemother making my nightly rounds." I squeaked out, "You are kidding." She assured me that she was not kidding and she did not seem amused as she shut the door and ambled down the hall to scare the next victim.

At Mercy, students were provided with meal cards for the hospital cafeteria where every morsel that was on our tray was recorded. I thought this was a good way for the hospital to be able to record expenses incurred by student nurses and maybe they could take it off as some kind of tax exemption.

I was unaware that they checked the cards to see what a student was consuming until one day when I was called to Sister Mary Ethel's office. Sister glared at my cafeteria card like it was on fire and said that this it was apparent that I did not see the value of healthy eating habits as was expected of students at Mercy Hospital School of Nursing. She pointed out that one glass of juice or not eating breakfast at all was not acceptable. Since I figured I was saving them money, I pointed this out and then told Sister that I preferred sleep to breakfast.

Sister Mary Ethel, in a stern voice, said in no uncertain terms that sleep was to lose and breakfast was to win. If I had a problem getting enough sleep then go to bed earlier. (This would have entirely cramped what was left of my social life.) I toyed with the idea of asking Mumme to use her card along with my own since she loved breakfast so much, but, as usual, Mumme was in enough trouble already. If I asked the two Niagara Falls girls, they would just do it to be nice and that wasn't fair to them as they didn't deserve to get in trouble. Mumme was more used to it.

Across from Sister Mary Ethel's office were several partitioned rooms where students could "entertain" gentlemen callers. "Entertaining" meant that no body parts could come into contact and proper conduct was to be observed at all times, and it was always observed by the vigilant Housemothers and the nuns. They neglected to notice, however, the behavior in the cars parked on the streets near the hospital between some of the students and the gentlemen predators, which was just as well.

And More Restrictions

In the dorm, including the lounge area, no one was allowed to wear shorts or slacks because an "un-ladylike" position might be assumed. This rule made little sense because you can assume some rather "un-ladylike" positions in nightgowns and skirts, too. The lounge in the dorm was like a "common area." We would meet to catch up on the latest news. As time went on, we would also pay attention to any additions to the rules and regulations or who had been "privileged" to meet with Sister Mary Ethel for a private conference.

The lounge was where we were allowed to smoke, which wasn't recognized yet as an unhealthy habit. Some of the ads even had doctors advertising a particular brand of cigarettes, which implied that they were the experts on smoking. This might make one consider whether their doctor could be a "Marlboro Man." To be fair, the research on the dangers of smoking wasn't conclusive at the time.

Marian Hall was the name of the building that housed the Nursing School and Dormitory. As we learned to live together, misunderstandings would happen, but we learned to solve them through laughter and tears. Gossip was repeated and generally forgotten unless it impinged directly on the person spreading it. The pressure of caring for the sick can be an anxiety provoking experience and we learned to listen to and support each other through the days that were difficult. In our allegiance, we found strength and trust.

After the initiation and indoctrination, students headed to the lounge to attempt to process the restrictions that were being enforced on their lives. If a Mercy student had planned to enjoy dorm life and all the freedom, she quickly discovered that she had somehow entered the convent.

Yolanda questioned the wisdom of the stringent rules that forced students to attempt to find ways around them. Emilie figured that if the nuns felt that they were important than they must be followed. Her friend Moe informed her that the nuns made rules so that they could catch you doing something wrong and that this made them feel good.

Mumme sat with a secretive smile while the wheels were turning at record speed in the overdeveloped "prank" part of her brain as she began her career as the master rule breaker. She eventually spent the most time in Sister Mary Ethel's office. This was never for friendly chats. She developed an impressive record of rule infractions. She was frequently campused—restricted to the dorm—which did not serve the nuns well since it provided extra time for her creative juices to flow.

One student was nicknamed Vera Good Cookie with good reason. Whenever she went home for a visit, she returned with the best homemade cookies in town to share. We would hear that Vera was back at the dorm and march to her room in order to help her eat all those delights. However, a colony of ants was also marching to her room to look for any crumbs that had fallen by the wayside.

The housekeeper dutifully reported this to the proper authorities, better known as the nuns, who proceeded to ban the cookies and that wonderful flow of sugar into our now unhappy stomachs. Actually, I think that later Vera snuck some of the contraband quietly back into the dorm.

The KGB did watch us. We signed in and out of the dorm, mostly to head for a beer at the local bar. We were attached to our desks at the assigned times. In the lounge, we wore the appropriate clothes and assumed ladylike positions—depending on your definition—as we were usually so tired that we draped ourselves over the chairs. If you wanted to avoid time with Sister Mary Ethel in her office, you followed the rules or you found a way not to get caught.

Battle of Wits

It didn't start out as a war against the nuns, but life in the dorm did become more interesting and definitely more humorous when Mumme began her career as master caper creator. She started on a small scale—probably to test the waters before moving to direct hits on the enemy. We learned that you can move all the furniture out of the room of an unsuspecting student while they were in the shower. This event took good organizational skills and quick reflexes. These are also the attributes of good nurses.

As time progressed, Mumme's creative juices were not being tested enough, so she had a need to move on to the bigger and better opportunities. As luck would have it, the nuns were available to provide these occasions. As her ideas gained momentum, she found it necessary to enlist other students in her pranks. She reveled in her role as commander-in-chief and she found willing classmates to join in her battle of wits.

Nun's Nuances

The Mercy Sister in charge of the library had taken command of that area and treated it like a military post. It seemed like she had more rules than books. No zippers were to be worn on clothing while visiting the library (as in the chapel) in case the offender might sit down and scratch a chair. Looking back on this, I finally realized that nuns did not have zippers on their apparel, at least ones that are visible. Kleenex was to be kept out of sight, as the urge to place it on a desk after being used, might overtake a visitor. Most students managed to follow the rules or take the other option, which was to stay out of the library when "the boss" was vigilantly checking her empire.

There were other nuns besides Sister Mary Ethel who were part of the faculty at Mercy. One named Sister Cyrilla, had a room in the dorm. No one was sure what she did to earn that dubious distinction, but we could only guess. She really did not seem to care if we broke a few of the rules of the dorm. We wondered if she might be breaking a few of them herself, but we could not figure out which ones.

One day she asked me to go to her room and get Anthony for her. I was amazed that she had someone named Anthony living in her room. "Pardon me Sister, but did you ask me to go to your room and find somebody named Anthony?" Sister Cyrilla turned to me with a devious smile and told me that she wanted her Anatomy textbook and Anthony was the author. It was becoming more apparent what might have earned her a room in the dorm.

The hospital chaplain taught us Medical Ethics. He was kind and understanding and somewhat tired of life among the nuns. He told us that the most boring time of the week was when he had to hear the nun's confessions. I hoped that the student nurses might have spiced up his boredom with their confessions, but most would not take that chance since they were afraid that he might recognize their voices.

From A to Z, Continually

At the end of three years at Mercy, all students were quite proficient at alphabetizing the class names. This skill would never become one of value in the nursing environment, but the instructors loved it as they checked off who was present and who was absent from class. Every class started with the A students shouting out their names in perfect order and proceeding through the alphabet until the Zs.

When we called out our names the first time in freshman year, it took several minutes and mistakes were evident but by the end of three years, we had it down to about 1 and 1/2 minutes with flawless precision. If you were at the end at the alphabet, you had an extra minute to show up for class but the A and Bs had better be on time. We also had the "kindness" to call out the names of those who might be absent. This had to be prearranged because if you filled in a name and the person showed up later, it was evident that something was amiss.

To this day so many years later, some of us can still recite the class names in perfect alphabetical order. I used to think that this would never prove to be a marketable skill until one day I was reading an advertisement for a file clerk and it actually said, "must have a working knowledge of the alphabet."

As freshman, each night at eight o'clock we were freed from our desks and left to our own devices, but always under the watchful eyes of the faculty and Housemothers. Some of us headed to the local South Buffalo pub to relax and have a few laughs.

Another Maureen O. (she did not have a nickname) and her roommate, Gerrie, would head for the shower every night about the same time every night. They would stop by the lounge and announce, "If Jim or Tom (or whoever they were dating) calls, please tell him that I am in the shower." Sometimes I worried that I would not remember who said it and who might be calling. I hope I never mixed up the names and put a damper on a romance.

In the 1960s, nurses were required to wear caps while on duty. So, near the end of our freshman year, there was a formal capping ceremony. Each nursing school had a distinct cap, which represented the individual school. One of the threats before capping was to remind students that if they were in any trouble, they would not be able to attend the ceremony to receive a cap, which was quite a dishonor.

We found that it was the student's responsibility to figure out how to keep this starched implement fastened to the top of her head while she bent down to check a patients output or a chest tube and also to keep the cap from getting tangled in IV tubing. Some days a student might walk by a mirror and realize that her professional appearance was as askew as the cap dangling from one side of her head.

It always seemed like some kind of miracle that the nurse on duty with the straightest cap was the one in charge. After time, it became apparent that the charge nurse did not have to climb around the beds so she could keep her head and hat on straight.

The Girdle Incident

It was an inanimate object but it took on a life of its own at Mercy. It started when I was attending Canisius College and I began to feel the familiar twinges of menstrual cramps. I was not thrilled with "the tears of my weeping womb" as they became more uncomfortable. I was wearing a panty girdle to help keep up my stockings that had a tendency to drape around my ankles. However, the girdle was adding to the now "monster" cramps and the only avenue of relief would be to remove it and put it in my coat pocket in the girl's lounge.

The next class was to begin in five minutes so I rushed into the lounge, removed the offensive item and placed it into what I thought was my coat pocket. The "monster" in my abdomen started to ease. After classes, I returned to the lounge at Canisius for my coat and realized that the girdle was gone. It took a minute to know that in my hurry, I had inadvertently placed it in the wrong coat.

In the meantime, Maryann K. was quite surprised to find some one's girdle in her coat pocket. She showed it to Maj, a serious student with a mischievous charm. They decided that this might be an opportunity to have a little fun. When they were back at Mercy, the conspirators took the elevator to the basement in the dorm. Laughing at their daring, they placed the girdle on a large bulletin board that was used for notices and threats and attached a note that read, "Does this belong to Sister Claver?"

They proceeded to the dorm lounge where they cajoled their classmates to check out the latest message on the bulletin board downstairs. Instead of finding a message on the bulletin board, their classmates were confronted by an angry Sister Mary Ethel carrying a girdle and demanding to know "Who is responsible for this?"

They reported back to the conspirators that Sister Mary Ethel was on the prowl and was looking for the guilty parties who dared this atrocious act. The schemers thought they were kidding until the next day when the class assembly began with

17

the threats..."Unless those who are responsible for this act come forward, the entire class will be campused," or "Unless those who are responsible for this act come forward, no one will receive their cap," and on and on just short of the electric chair.

Out of their generous natures the "criminals" came forward and admitted their guilt for the grievous incident. It must be stated here that there was nothing in the Mercy Student Handbook about placing girdles on bulletin boards. The Handbook does state "Students are responsible for knowledge of all material on official bulletin boards in the school. Permission must be obtained from the School of Nursing Office for posting of any notices in Marian Hall and from the Administrator for posting of same in any part of the hospital."

This must have been a simple oversight on the part of the conspirators. They were campused and they received a long and thorough lecture on their infamous activity. The girdle bearer was also punished. Eventually, Sister Mary Ethel must have figured that the punishment was enough and she paroled the prisoners. On Valentine's Day, I was thrilled to see a gift in my mailbox. I wondered if it was from my boyfriend who attended college out of town. However, it was that lousy girdle which I proceeded to destroy.

Friendships

Friendships were formed at Mercy that lasted through many years. We have laughed and cried together, shared our joy and also our sorrows in a bond of close sisterhood. We learned from each other that caring is one of our best attributes and that attitude can make a difficult situation into a triumph.

As we look back at that dorm experience and see how we were always under some one's scrutiny, we are now able to see it in a new light. We played the usual pranks that dorm life creates, such as putting peanut butter on the toilet seats. We tried waking up a tired student during the long dark winter and tell her that it was time to get up because the night shift supervisor had called and was looking for her, when in actuality the shift did not start for another five hours.

Several of us took a trip to Washington, DC in our senior year. Mary Anne W. convinced us to attend a Congressional session. We then went to the underground part of the Capitol and the next thing we knew Mary Anne was traveling on a railroad car with three senators in all her glory. Afterwards, she explained who the senators were and which states they represented. The rest of us, who were not as knowledgeable in political affiliations, were amazed since we could barely manage to name our own state senators.

Kathy M. sang opera arias in the shower and that helped to relax us and enjoy her beautiful voice, especially those of us who were only acquainted with "rock and roll." By senior year, many were engaged and displayed their engagement rings with pride while some of us were happy to feel free. The Mercy Handbook clearly stated, "Students who wish to marry must resign from the school." The infamous handbook stated that the student "must see herself as a religious person, as a professional person, and as a social person." Apparently they felt that marriage might interfere with the religious, the professional, the social, or possibly all three.

In the dorm at Mercy, all phone calls went through the switchboard and were answered by the Housemother who then announced over a loud speaker (when it was not during the hours assigned for study) that Miss ----- had a call. Time on the phone was supposed to be limited, so anyone awaiting an "important" call would police the student on the phone. There was a pay phone on each floor but it was usually occupied. This seems so archaic now in the light of cell phones and texting.

Knowledge Gaps

In high school when the nun that taught us Biology announced that next week we would be studying the reproductive system and human sexuality, we really looked forward to the lecture. We were "all ears" until we realized she was describing mitosis of the cell and cell division and none of the "good stuff."

My friends from high school called me one evening at Mercy because they knew that I was in a nursing course and they needed to fill in some of the many gaps in their lack of sexual knowledge. This may have still been limited to mitosis of the cell or "French" kissing. They had a list of questions regarding unfamiliar anatomical territory and hoped that I would be able to fill in their curiosity or to confirm what they thought they had learned from some books they had found while babysitting. I told them that I had no idea and no way was I about to ask the professor or any of the other student nurses. I never did ask any of them if they had found the answers, but since most of them are married now with children, it is apparent that they are better informed.

One classmate had come into the lounge one night after a date and stated that she could not understand why so many guys carried pencils in their pockets and when they kissed her good night, she could feel the pencil hit her leg. I think someone suggested that she must be dating a lot of students. Because of incidents like this, I knew better than to check out any "knowledge gaps" with my innocent dorm sisters.

Retreat Capers

As senior students, we were assigned to attend a two-day spiritual retreat in order to spend time in a quiet contemplative atmosphere for personal renewal. By this time in our training we were ready to be open to the world rather than retreat from it.

Silence was enforced at the retreat and there wasn't even a chance to sin if you didn't count the impure thoughts. The Mercy bus carried the group of twenty-year-old hormonal women to the retreat house. We sang our favorite songs on the bus including popular drinking songs or songs about missing our boyfriends and what we would do when we saw them after this "prolonged" absence. We sang loud and mostly off key, except for Kathy M. who had wanted to be a professional singer but her mother thought nursing would be a better career. The lyrics left a lot to be desired but we wanted to put our "naughty" selves in song to counteract the effects of the retreat.

Sister Rita greeted us. Apparently, she was not totally fond of her job and even less fond of those who entered her prison to reflect on their wayward behaviors. She must have also thought we were illiterate because she proceeded to read each and every rule that was posted on the surrounding walls. We waged bets about the last time that she had smiled. Mumme said it must have been in utero and it was probably just gas.

We sat down to our first meal at the retreat as Sister Rita started the record player and out of that ancient machine came a sugary voice that emanated with the words, "Where God is, love is." Every time we picked up our forks, the record played until one day, Mumme whispered to me that it was getting to her. "Are you thinking what I'm thinking?" she inquired. "That record is much too slow. Let's speed it up and help Sister to flex her frown muscles."

As we sat down to another meal at the retreat, Sister Rita proceeded to the record player and it did not help that she peered out at us with a look of total disdain. It encouraged us to know that in time we would earn her personal distaste for us.

I was the lookout while Mumme managed to find the right buttons to "improve" the recording. At the next meal, garbled words replaced the solemn message, which caused a loud burst of spontaneous laughter from everyone except Sister Rita. With the speed of lightening, she quickly silenced the machine and glared at the raucous participants with undisguised disgust.

"I know what you have done here. You think that I don't see your shenanigans but I am well aware of them. You moved the statues to one of your rooms. You are whispering when you think that I can't hear. And now this-this-this newest incident...I intend to report this to your director," and she proceeded to threaten to inform the FBI, the President and anyone else who might not be interested and of course anyone who could hear her. This included most of the Western Hemisphere. Mumme looked at me and exclaimed, "Maybe we can help Sister find her sense of humor by short sheeting her bed tonight!"

Medicine from Hell

The Mercy Student Handbook stated, "The aim of the health service is to improve and conserve the health of the student in the school." I found that they were vigilant in providing students with health service. I was called to Sister Claver's office one day and told that my chest x-ray showed an area that needed to be looked at with more in depth x-rays.

This included following the instructions included in the x-ray preparations. The first instruction was to drink a bottle of castor oil emulsion. The bottle looked innocent enough with a white oily substance. At the designated time, I downed the castor oil, which made the hospital food taste like a gourmet delight. I then proceeded to have an emesis of the entire bottle. I returned to Sister Claver to explain what had happened. Sister unfortunately was quickly able to provide another bottle of white oily fluid.

I attempted plugging my nose, positive thinking and deep breathing exercises to get that bottle down, but it came to the same end. I was glad I was dealing with Sister Claver because she was kind and understanding. Sister appeared sympathetic and suggested I plug my nose and try a positive frame of mind to keep the medicine down (already done), and as luck would have it, she had a third bottle of that wretched medicine right in her office. This time out of sheer persistence I kept the medicine down because I knew that the health office had an endless supply of it.

That night, the students had planned a dance at the school to raise some money for the class treasury and some also hoped to meet their soul mates. I decided that instead of dancing, my time would be in the closest bathroom because my cramps were telling me that the Castor oil had "reached" my other end…so much for meeting a soul mate.

Chapter Four

Canisius College

Storm Warning Ahead – A Deluge of Men

During freshman year at Mercy, we attended classes at Canisius College where Sister Mary Ethel had pointed out that the ratio of males to females was 10:1. This might sound like a dream situation. However, most of us had just graduated from an all-girls high school, so we were not comfortable in this unfamiliar territory. In fact, the landscape at Canisius felt about as familiar as a lunar landing. Since the males in this college were well aware of having the upper hand, they made the most of the situation and found great joy in embarrassing the nurses until we managed to fight back or one of them had fallen head over heels for a nursing student. This definitely changed his perspective.

Brotherly Love

My brother attended Canisius so he managed to keep any possible suitor away from his innocent sister. When I was home on weekends and waiting by the phone for a call from some wonderful prospect, his innate antenna seemed to know when I had abandoned my post near the phone for a brief minute.

He would inform my dream caller that I had been put in my cage and would be out in about two weeks. Then he would tell the caller that he understood that the caller wouldn't want to be bothered to call back as no one ever did. His other favorite form of torture was to answer the phone and call me and then yell out in a loud voice, "It's a boy for a change although why would one call you?" This could put a damper on any social life. I considered becoming a nun but I didn't want to be challenged by students like Mumme or spend the rest of my life in the convent.

As we settled into our collegiate classes, we realized why we were expected to study at our desks for three hours every night.

Chemistry, Microbiology, English, Sociology, Logic, Anatomy and Physiology were not an easy course load. Along with this load, we had to keep up on our outside interests and stay out of the nun's way, all of which equaled my brother's attempts to keep me home on weekends.

Anatomy and Physiology

My favorite course at Canisius College was Anatomy and Physiology, which was taught by a lay professor, Dr. Stouter. As difficult as this subject was, he started me on a lifelong love of the study of human Anatomy and Physiology.

It was fascinating to sit in class and hear about these bodily processes and realize that they were all going on inside of me. If Dr. Stouter was lecturing about the heart, I would become acutely aware that I could feel it beating or as he was talking about the respiratory system, I felt my chest rise with each inspiration. Other systems and organs were less accessible. It took some imagination to picture the liver or gallbladder at work.

However, this course taught me to have a definite life-long dislike of the smell of formaldehyde. During Anatomy lab, we were arranged in groups of three and told that we would be dissecting cats that had spent their time after life in a bath of formaldehyde. To say that we were not exactly enthusiastic would be a gross understatement. Anyone who had a cat for a pet now saw that same animal in a different light. They had injected a substance into the kitty so the veins appeared blue and the arteries appeared red. During the beginning of the semester, the smell was vaguely pungent but by the end of the year in the warmer weather, the formaldehyde had a way of remaining in our nasal passages until the end of the day.

One group decided to place a butterscotch lifesaver in the cat's bladder to see what would happen. Thinking that they were ingenious, they called the lab assistant over at the last class and asked what he thought the phenomena might be. The lab assistant was most enthusiastic to see that the cat had two ureters on the right side, which the group had missed in deference to the butterscotch lifesaver.

Sociology

Sociology was taught by a Jesuit priest who seemed to have the idea that the nursing students should be the ones to populate the earth. Possibly, he felt that Eve was the first nurse and we should follow in her footsteps. He repeatedly told us menstruation was "the tears of a weeping womb." Since we were not allowed to be pregnant or married in the nursing school, our wombs must have been having some good cries.

If a student did not have the right answer for any of his questions ready, he would say in a loud voice, "That is a ZIP for you." He informed us that each day as we entered class, we would be expected to sing a song that he would assign on the day before. We were a group of women that were trying to be as inconspicuous as possible and appearing as the daily sociology choir did not help. One day he assigned a song titled "At the End of a Perfect Day." No one had heard of it and no one wanted to have all those "ZIPS" for not singing.

Mumme came to the rescue as she wrote a classic for Sociology:

> At the end of a perfect day
> No more Sociolo-J
> With a weary sigh, we cry hip hip hip hooray
> No more zips for us poor chill'n
> From good old Father Cantillon
> There is nothing more to say
> At the end of a perfect day.

As luck would have it, he loved the song and asked for repeat performances.

Microbes All Night

Microbiology was the toughest course and most of us spent the entire night before the exam studying quietly with a flashlight under the covers in case the Housemother decided to visit. Learning about life under a microscope was like studying a new galaxy. After three in the morning, we just put on the lights and pulled out the textbooks. We then proceeded to the chapel to ask for divine intervention. Kathy M. did not seem concerned as she sang opera in the shower the night before and produced her usual A grade. Most of us did well on the exam which made me realize that divine intervention works even in microbiology.

Irish Charm

One of our favorite priests at Canisius was the Prefect of Discipline. He must have been tired of dealing with all of the adolescent hormonal males and their behavior. However, he loved dealing with the nursing students who were afraid to do anything that might get them referred to Sister Mary Ethel who had discipline perfected.

Since most of the Mercy students had some connection to South Buffalo, which was a predominately Irish neighborhood, he would carry a map of Ireland and then check your name against his name to see where your ancestors ranked in comparison to his family. It was some time later when we figured out that his family name must have been the highest ranked on that particular map because his family always won, which caused him to walk on with Irish pride.

The Storm Ends

After a year, the bus pulled out of the parking lot at Canisius for the last time and we felt some regrets. Some of us were dating Canisius students and would end up marrying them. Others enjoyed the attention even if it tended to be embarrassing. Moe O. and Judy S. remained faithful to their boyfriends at Notre Dame, which was good for the rest of us. They were very pretty and fun loving and could have had a date with anybody at Canisius, if they cared to venture down that avenue. Those of us who were dating Canisius students told Moe and Judy that it might not be worth it.

Chapter Five

Clinicals

Practice Doesn't Always Make Perfect

Mercy Hospital has a definite presence in South Buffalo. The immense yellow brick building was enough to intimidate most student nurses and it was particularly unnerving to a first year student, especially if she was directionally challenged. As with most hospitals, it was a place that most people prefer to avoid (there are exceptions to this rule), but if you needed medical care, it was acknowledged as the "place to be."

The sights, sounds and scents of the first days spent at Mercy have remained with me throughout the years. I am grateful that the pungent odor of waxed floors and strong disinfectants has been taken over by the more acceptable alternatives that are now available in hospitals.

Mercy was named for the nuns that presided over the vast array of Mercy's services and they were dedicated to making sure that their reputation remained untarnished. They took pride in the fact that the medical care was not only adequate, but also exceptional.

We did not understand why the doctors never liked July. It seemed like a nice warm month, especially in Buffalo. However, the new interns started that month and the latest batch of student nurses were entering their domain. Somehow practicing in a nursing lab and being in a real life situation at times seemed worlds apart.

One student was assigned to walk a patient who was starting to recover from a stroke. As they reached a point about half way down the hall, the patient indicated that she had to vomit. The student thought, maybe I missed the part about carrying an emesis basin with me at all times so she held out her hands and told the patient to go ahead and vomit so that she wouldn't choke. As the patient proceeded to vomit in her hands, the medical director of the hospital walked by and yelled in a loud voice, "Someone get a nurse and bring a basin." The student was upset that he did not recognize that she was in control of the situation and that she was a nursing student even if her hands were full of bodily fluid. It was part of the job.

Another student was only too glad to help a doctor who was preparing to apply a cast on a patient's arm. At that time, it was necessary to soak the roll of plaster-filled gauze in water, in order to start the process so the plaster would mold to whatever limb was broken. The student found the appropriate pail and filled it with water.

However, she failed to realize that the doctor would not appreciate scalding hot water. As he plunged the plaster into the pail, he was heard to exclaim, "My hands, my hands!" He then threw the plaster roll up in the air where it landed on the light above. Probably he was using some stronger language under his breath and it should be noted that he did not thank the student for her help.

Almost Reality

One of the surgeons was enlisted to teach us about trauma nursing. He was a typical surgeon because he seemed to really love all types of gadgets and equipment and he brought a whole arsenal with him into the classroom. He presented several different scenarios and he relished the fact that as a student examined the abdomen on the mannequin, a supposed loop of bowel would pop out. If an arm appeared injured when another student went to check it, the arm would fall off. Sometimes, a large amount of red fluid resembling blood would gush from a limb.

The man was in his element and as the class progressed we really learned quite a lot about the many possibilities of trauma nursing. At the end of class, he started to pack up his many supplies when he noted a large red stain on the floor. We then realized he was one of us. He was also afraid of the nuns as he called out in a loud surgical voice for scouring powder and buckets. He was down on the floor quickly, showing more elbow grease than the best housekeeper.

At times, practicing in the clinical lab seemed like it might border on reality. However, anyone who tells you that practicing giving injections into an orange is the same as giving one to a human buttock is not familiar with anatomy. After practicing with the oranges, we eventually had to face the day of telling some poor unsuspecting patient to roll over while they were treated to the first experience of a student nurse giving a "real" injection. Actually, there was a moment when the patient rolled over and lifted his gown when you almost expected that an orange would appear. It was quite a surprise for the first time to see skin and buttocks appear like in the textbook pictures.

One student was particularly proud of the fact that she managed to be professional and calm while attempting this daunting task. She told the patient to roll over, lined up the buttock and managed to get the syringe to its intended spot. After removing the syringe, she took a deep sigh while her nursing instructor pointed out that she forgot to inject the medicine.

We were taught Fundamentals of Nursing in a large classroom with uncomfortable chairs. A large life-size doll named Mrs. Chase was our patient. Mary Lee decided to move Mrs. Chase one day before class. She then took over Mrs. Chase's bed for the class and the instructor who happened to be Sister Claver, did not notice. The class was afraid to laugh because we didn't want Mary Lee to be campused for the rest of her life at Mercy. She found the bed much more comfortable than those infamous chairs.

Bed Bath

As Sister Claver started to teach us the fine art of giving a bed bath, it seemed simple enough. It was easy in the classroom while practicing on Mrs. Chase, who never moved unless you moved her. We listened carefully because this was something that we would have to do soon on "real" people. It actually didn't even look like it would take any significant amount of skill like giving an injection. We headed to the hospital to attempt to put into practice what we had learned.

I greeted my first bed bath patient with a cheery, "Good morning! I am here to freshen you up and give you a bath." The patient was happy to start with her dentures, which she quickly took out and handed to me. I stared at the objects in my hand for a minute before I recovered and then I headed for the bathroom, which was locked because another patient was in it. Since I couldn't hand the patient her unclean dentures, I tightly clasped them in one hand and found a denture cup. The bathroom was eventually vacated and the dentures were shiny, but not before the patient's doctor came in to talk to her and wondered if she had a stroke until he realized she was just talking without dentures.

Next, it was time to fill the basin with water, so I filled it to the top and then managed to spill most of it on the way back to the patient. She found this quite amusing and suggested that I might want to try using less water in the basin. "Of course, what was I thinking?" I responded. The next time I decided that a few tablespoons of water might work better. The patient also found this quite amusing. She was able to wash herself except for her back so all went well after that. She really liked the fifteen minute back rub and told me that no one had ever given her such a thorough back rub so now she knew that she could expect one every day.

Finally the experience was in the past and the patient said she really had fun with this one and she couldn't wait to tell her family. I headed down the hall for case conference and the instructor asked me where I had been since the conference was almost over. I replied that I was bathing my patient and the instructor commented that the patient must be the cleanest on the floor. I thought that may be true, especially her teeth. I wondered if this was my punishment for laughing at the nuns.

Catheters, Enemas and Explanations

We would be taught many nursing procedures. The infamous Nursing Policy and Procedure Manual would be frequently in our hands while we tried to figure how to incorporate all the words that described a procedure in exact terms, into our patient care.

It is hard to imagine what to do with a catheterization kit when you have to open it and then don sterile gloves. It is important to explain everything to the patient, both before the procedure and as you perform the technique, while trying to have a calm, professional demeanor. One patient, upon hearing that she was about to be catheterized replied, "I have never been castrated before." Credit is always given to those who do not laugh at such remarks while in a professional stance.

It never seemed to fail that as the student explained, for the first time, to a patient that she would be placing a Foley catheter that the patient would state, "Oh, I've had that done before and they always have trouble with it. Do you have a lot of experience with catheters?" This did not bring a feeling of confidence to a rookie.

We studied the policy and procedure manual carefully and learned both the science and art of nursing with the help of instructors and staff. It was especially difficult to do anything to a patient that we knew to be inherently painful.

Enemas were another area (excuse the reference) where the classroom and reality are at odds. It looked so innocuous when you place some warm water in a plastic container after making sure that the attached tubing is clamped and you then lubricate the part to enter the patient's rectum, hold up the container and unclamp the tubing and voila, the results are magnificent. This works well if you are ambidextrous and remember every word of the class and the procedure manual.

However, in reality many of us forgot to clamp the tubing and were drenched along with the patient and the results may not have been magnificent. One common type of enema in those days was called a Triple H enema, that stood for "high, hot, and a hell of a lot." Even a student knew better than to want that assignment and most patients weren't fond of it either.

We were reminded to explain everything to a patient before we performed any procedure. We tried to be reassuring, but it was a bit disconcerting at first. One student was working on a surgical floor (in those days, the surgeons did not have the advantages of some of the techniques for minimizing scarring from the operation) and the patient was concerned about the scar from her upcoming surgery. She told the patient not to worry about her appendectomy scar, because they were minimal, but if it were gallbladder surgery, it would be a lot worse. You guessed it; the patient was having gallbladder surgery.

Operating Room Observation

I was so excited the first morning that I was scheduled to observe in the operating room. I could hardly wait to see if it was like the programs on TV with everyone gowned and gloved with masks on so no one knew who they were.

Observation in the operating rooms could be fascinating or frightening to student nurses, some who would faint when textbook anatomy became a three dimensional reality. I was watching an abdominal operation when I became totally immersed in the display of the inside workings of that anatomical area. I inched closer to get a better look. I was amazed and totally engrossed.

Suddenly, I realized that the surgeon was calling in a loud voice and repeating himself. He sounded exasperated as he yelled out "Miss, Miss Can you see?" All of a sudden I realized he was talking to me. "Oh, yes," I replied innocently and with great enthusiasm. I thought that he was being kind until he repeated his question in a much louder voice and then told me that it was nice that I could see everything because he couldn't see and he was the surgeon. Chagrined to the core, I stepped back out of the way.

Sister Jean's Territory

Sister Jean Baptist was in charge of the obstetrical floor and she considered anyone who entered that area as part of her domain. This included patients, visitors, doctors, nurses, student nurses and anyone who got off the elevator to enter her territory.

She had the Catholic attitude that the more babies in a family "the merrier" which meant that the nursery area should always be full. A large picture of "the holy family" loomed above the main desk. Above the picture was a light. When things started to slow down, Sister Jean would turn that light on and it seemed that almost immediately the mothers would be coming in and ready to deliver. After several hours of many deliveries, one of the staff would check to see if Sister Jean had left "her territory." If the coast were clear, she would then reach up and shut off the light so the staff could take a much-needed break.

Psychiatric Training, A World Away

We went to a private hospital about twenty-five miles north of New York City for Psychiatric training. In our junior year, one quarter of the class was assigned to this affiliation for three months at a time. Most of us were still innocent of the "real world" as we stepped off the plane or train in New York City and headed to Harrison, New York. We hoped the rules would be more relaxed and that the buses or trains would head for the big city frequently because we wanted to be on them. For several of us, it was not only our first plane flight or train trip but also the longest we had been away from home.

Some of the class had "fallen" in like or love for the first and sometimes the last time. They spent many hours writing long letters to that special person or waiting for a phone call from him. They counted the days until they returned home again or their "Mr. Wonderful" came to visit Harrison.

Some of us saw this as an opportunity to see the world and see some of the real world we did, by visiting New York City or hitchhiking, with thumbs outstretched, to the local town for a beer. We only hitchhiked if there were several of us along the road. Never cognizant of the danger of this method of transportation, we only knew we were broke and it was a way to see something outside the grounds of the psychiatric hospital.

Earning money meant babysitting in the nearby wealthy community where the kids had more money in their piggy banks than any student nurse had in her purse. Some of these cherubs tended to be a lively group who were used to student nurses as babysitters and felt it was their chance to see if they could test the household rules. They did not realize that these student nurses were wise to these games, as they had expertly tested most rules themselves under the careful guidance of Miss Mumme.

The real-world of psychiatric nursing is necessary as part of the education of every nurse. Not only does this make the student aware of the mind-body connection, it also allows the beginning of understanding of how fragile that connection might be. It expands an awareness of how important it is to listen and to suspend judgment until we can begin to try to comprehend mental illness.

Psychiatric medicine was limited at that time compared to the barrage of prescriptions available today. We watched as patients underwent electroshock therapy. One instructor explained that if someone is paranoid and believes that you have written something about them on a piece of paper, even if you show them the blank paper, they will still say that they see the words. I wondered about this, but decided not to test the theory as the instructor had years of experience in psychiatric nursing and I'd had about two weeks.

Many of us struggled to comprehend the world of Freud and the complexities of the mind. Since our days at Mercy and clinical rotations were usually determined by where you fit into the alphabetical order in the class, I was part of the last group in the psychiatric rotation.

We were warned about some of the instructors, one of whom would often turn to an unsuspecting student and shout "WATCH OUT, WATCH OUT OR YOU'LL REACT." I was so determined not to let this instructor see my reaction that I stared straight ahead if she tried to elicit a reaction. She may have thought that I had catatonic tendencies.

The psychiatric clinical rotation was disliked intensely by some second year nursing students, while others found it interesting and challenging. As in many situations that we face in life, fear about what might happen is worse than what did happen.

A Scary Night

I remember working on a chronic ward one night with Judy, a student nurse from a hospital near Syracuse, New York, when the sound of someone tapping on a window became annoying. The tapping continued for several minutes until it began to fray the calmest nerves including those on major tranquilizers. Even second year nursing students realized that disturbing any peace on a psychiatric unit was not in the best interest of anyone. (In those days, students were sometimes left in charge of this type of unit.)

Judy enlisted me to follow her to the source of the noise. We entered a dark room where the only light was from the full moon outside. Judy approached the patient, who was dressed entirely in black and who was continuing to tap, tap, and tap. In a calm voice Judy asked her to stop. She did stop, turned around and in a high pitched voice and strange laugh managed to sound like the lead character in a horror show. Judy screamed and ran straight into me like a football tackler and then pulled me from the room.

After stopping to assess our personal damages of fast heart rates and rapid breathing along with some sore muscles, we realized that we did achieve our goal as the patient stopped tapping and soon afterwards went to bed. We were still shaking a half hour later.

Dancing "in the Dark"

Some days were enjoyable as we played cards with patients or took them for walks outside. One assignment was to travel to a nearby mental hospital and attend a dance with the patients. As we boarded the bus that took us there, many of us felt the pangs of anxiety. Maybe this assignment was to help us understand what it feels like to be anxious or possibly they were in need of a few more inpatients so they were putting us to the test.

When we arrived, they explained that many patients attended the dance for fun or to meet someone. Others just wanted to have someone available to light their cigarettes. Smoking, again, was not recognized as a health hazard and some even felt it helped in calming or relaxing a person. Therefore, the patients were allowed cigarettes but someone else had to light them, because they did recognize the danger of fire.

To this day, I am not sure if this was for the benefit of the patient or the nursing student. It was a great ego booster because no one sat out a dance and every student had at least one or two patients asking for each dance. It was actually a lot of fun and several of us admitted it was better than some of our dates.

An X-Rated Patient Study

As an assignment, we were told to pick out a patient and begin to write down our interactions with that patient in a notebook in order to be able to look at how we communicated with the patient. This was called a POS or Patient Observation Study. Sara S. chose a patient who expressed her feelings with every known four-letter word. She could have made the entire Navy blush because she also had a unique way of combining the words. The first time I encountered her she shouted, "I want to take a bath with J_____ C_____."

I remember thinking that I did not always understand what she meant, although as time has progressed, I now know she managed to put the most explicit words together for shock value. Because this patient had several issues with anger, Sara's notebook could have been x-rated. Being conscientious and with a gleam in her eye, Sara wrote down each and every word that was uttered. Needless to say, in this Catholic institution, the nursing instructor wrote a comment in large red letters instructing Sara to leave out the curse words. This made her notes very short.

Chapter Six

End of the Beginning
or the Beginning of the End

Light at the End of the Tunnel

When the last group left Harrison, New York for home, it was to face senior year and more responsibility. Sister Mary Ethel no longer cared what we ate for breakfast, but she did care what we were doing in our clinical rotations. She probably did believe in miracles as Miss Mumme was still in the program and both had survived the battle of wits. In fact, Miss Mumme was turning out to be a fine nurse, although she still seemed to test the waters of institutional mandates.

Looking back on how nursing was practiced so many years ago compared to today could fill another book. We did not have automatic IV pumps, so we counted drops by the minute to figure out the infusion rate. Critical Care Units had not come into their own, so the sickest patients were often placed nearest to the nurse's station. Patients remained in bed for long periods after coronary events and surgery until clinicians realized that it is usually healthier to get out of bed than stay on bed rest. Mothers stayed in the hospital for several days after giving birth.

Calculations that today are tabulated quickly by the touch of a computer, in those days were equations that we figured out by hand and then checked with one another. Nursing has caught up with the times. It still is not an easy career, but it remains a rewarding one.

Looking back over those three years, they seemed to have disappeared like a flash of light. However, while we were enduring those years, they seemed to last forever or maybe even longer.

As senior nursing students, we had more responsibility and accountability and the same amount of freedom. The rules remained inflexible so it became even more challenging to find ways around them. They kept us busy and tired which helped to keep us out of trouble as much as possible.

Several students came into the dorm with a dreamy look in their eyes and a shiny engagement ring on their left hand. "Congratulations!" would echo throughout the dorm. However, others felt that they wanted time to experience the "world" and looked forward to freedom and life at the beach or the ski slopes before settling down to a nest.

Many nights in the lounge were dedicated to discussion of what we would do after graduation like sleep for a week, read a novel of our own choosing for a change, or even be wild enough to wear shorts without a coat over them in public. We began to look at the graduate nurses as real human beings with lives of their own outside of the hospital, something we had not experienced in quite a while.

It began to look like there might be life beyond nursing school and the infamous hospital tunnel. It might even mean finding a job and getting paid which would definitely be a new experience. Nurses in the hospital suddenly seemed friendlier, possibly because we had finally managed to speak in a voice above a whisper to them.

Toward the end of senior year, we applied for our first jobs, which also meant we would be getting a paycheck. We were told it would be best to spend the first year after training in a hospital setting to get more experience. Since most us were down to our last dollar by this time, we went back home to live with our parents. If the parental scene could be stricter than Mercy, it would be a real feat of authority.

We would think about how we would spend the $2.00 dollars an hour that we would earn. Mumme, ever the original creator of ideas wanted to go find Tara from *Gone with the Wind*, a book she had lived in for the last three years. With a weary sigh, Mumme agreed that Rhett Butler, Scarlett O'Hara, and Tara were fictional and it would be difficult, and in fact impossible, to find them even if they did seem to come alive on those pages by Margaret Mitchell.

Our Graduation Day

> It was a day to forget and a day to remember
> A day to look back and a day to reach forward
> A day to feel down and a day to look up
> A day for endings and a day for new beginnings
> A day to say goodbye and a lifetime to
> reconnect

Graduation Day in June 1963 was sunny and bright as sixty-six Mercy students prepared for their graduation ceremony at St. Thomas Church on Abbott Road in South Buffalo. Actually, the nuns had us practice for several days leading up to the commencement just in case one of us might get any unusual or inventive ideas. Looking back over the three years stirred up memories of fun and laughter, but most of us would choose to leave behind the more challenging days.

We had cleared the Mercy dorm of our belongings so other students could lay claim to our cells. All of the rules were still posted but we would no longer have to abide by them. Rules are imposed upon us throughout life, but we didn't know that as we started to bask in what seemed like a newfound freedom. As we lined up for the procession into the church, we were all wearing the same starched white graduation uniform (and the same chafed neck) with the Mercy Hospital symbol of a starched white cap perched on our heads.

Sister Mary Ethel looked at "her" students with an air of pride. Actually, her vigilant eyes scanned the graduates until they rested on Ms. Mumme. She looked like she was pondering the fact that this was graduation day and Ms. Mumme might be able to resist a caper or possibly it was relief that their three-year "battle of the wills" was finally over. It was the usual type of ceremony with family and friends in attendance and awards given for whatever the nuns felt were valuable attributes in the class (pranks by students were not on the list).

There is Life after Mercy

We had become Mercy Nurses in three short formative years. We now understood that we could look forward to the physical and mental challenges of our chosen career. However, Mercy also taught us that caring is the most important part of nursing and if you understand that, then everything else falls into place. As I traveled with my parents over the familiar territory between Mercy and home, I thought of all the fears I had harbored on my original journey to Mercy Hospital School of Nursing. I was glad that I didn't know then that I would have to face many of those demons and conquer them.

Some members of the class would remain active in nursing for over four decades while others chose to leave nursing behind with Mercy. The experiences of those years would change us forever and we might have known that in June 1963, but we probably did not realize how deep those roots were planted.

Many had formed friendships that would last a lifetime while others parted and never crossed paths again. Bonds had formed as we shared joys and sorrows during those three formative years. The experiences at Mercy taught us how to support each other and we continued to do so through the pressures of nursing and through the triumphs and tragedies in our individual lives. Louise S. reminds us of the importance of staying connected when some of us get together for lunch.

First Jobs

As days turn into years, the memory of a first nursing job is forever in a nurse's memory. Several of the class stayed at Mercy for those experiences. Moe O. and Emilie returned to Niagara Falls to their families and their boyfriends. Others went to work at another Mercy hospital north of Buffalo named Kenmore Mercy.

Mumme and I began our careers on the pediatric floor of Kenmore Mercy, along with our classmate, Gerrie. Gerrie had a ready smile and instilled confidence in patients and families as well as staff. I think several of our small patients decided to become nurses after being cared for by her. Mumme and I were more of the characters on the pediatric floor.

After we had worked long enough to earn money for a vacation, Gerrie, Pat G., Sheila, Kathy (a nurse from Sisters of Charity Hospital) and I decided to travel to Fort Lauderdale, Florida for spring break. Fort Lauderdale was supposed to be *Where the Boys Are* according to a popular movie of the time, so that seemed like a good enough incentive for where the girls wanted to be. Gerrie had talked to two guys from Buffalo who were also planning on being in South Florida during spring break, so she mentioned where we were staying.

When we arrived at our hotel, those Buffalo guys were walking across the parking lot. I remember thinking that we had traveled over one thousand miles to meet "boys" who lived near home. I did not know then that Gerrie and I would still be married to them as I write this memoir.

The Capers Continue

Mumme still liked to try out a caper but her victims had changed. She was in love. Actually she had practiced writing her future married name on most of her notebooks during our senior year and she now had the signature so perfect that it would make a calligrapher jealous.

One time, her love was traveling out of town by train with friends to see a football game and Mumme decided she wanted to check up on him. She convinced me that we should disguise ourselves as two aged ladies and hide at the train station in a phone booth when he was expected to return. I was a bit nervous because if he did not return or there were females in their group, then Mumme would have wasted all that time practicing writing her "hoped for" next signature. He did get off the train with his male friends as planned, and the two "aged ladies" snuck out of the train station.

Mumme was inventive and also enthusiastic when she cared about someone or something. Robert Kennedy was coming to a political rally in Buffalo and she decided that it was imperative that she be there with me. She had spent a good part of the day making "Vote For Kennedy" signs. When I stopped to pick her up, I asked what we would use to carry the signs. Ever creative, Mumme reached up and took the sheer curtains off a nearby curtain rod and attached the signs.

She also taught me how to drive with commands like red means stop, green means go and yellow means go like hell. I informed her that they had left that out of the driving manual, but I also knew that a lot of her lessons on life were not in any books.

When we began raising our young families and feeling exhausted from the demands of toddlers, the drudgery of housework and the decisions of our jobs, we convinced our husbands that they needed some special time with the children without our interference. We then headed to Toronto to "get away from it all."

Mumme always was in search of the "perfect" hotel and as we headed away on a trip, she would announce that this time she had found it. I should have known better. She informed me that this one did not even charge for parking. I was awakened in the middle of the night by the sound of a crash. When I asked her what it was, she told me "she was killing the cockroaches." I informed her that I would rather pay for parking than room with cockroaches.

During another escape to a "perfect" hotel, I did manage to point out that the antiques in the place were lovely. However, I found it necessary to mention that the sheets on her bed appeared soiled, probably from a previous occupant.

Chapter Seven

Looking Back to Go Forward

Resurfacing Retreat House

I was in a yoga class on the top floor of The Himalayan Institute on Delaware Avenue in Buffalo, on a beautiful spring day, about forty-five years after our senior retreat. As I prepared to do a balancing posture, I briefly glanced out the window and felt the hair on my arms stand up straight.

I lost my concentration and my balance as I realized that across the street was a building that had become a significant part in the memories of my nursing school class.

The Mercy Retreat House was still in existence with a new sign in front but with the same foreboding presence. Wait until I tell Mumme and Moe that another of our old haunts is still around, I thought. I knew that they would want a tour and I was a bit concerned because I thought the place felt like it had ghosts over forty years ago and they probably had made a permanent home there.

I considered keeping the information to myself, but as luck would have it, at our next meeting they talked about finding the retreat house like they were detectives on a mission. I decided to tell them of the "probable" find and they both began to salivate as they made plans for the excursion.

As we drove down Delaware Avenue in Buffalo, we found the large mansion easily. The posted sign out front read "Child and Family Services." We decided to walk in and see if the interior matched our memories of the place where we had attended that infamous two-day religious retreat. We became totally convinced when we saw the spiral staircase that led to the second floor. We approached the receptionist at the front desk and asked her if this mansion was once the Mercy Retreat House. She informed us that she was not aware of the history of the mansion, but she was able to give us several names and phone numbers of women who could answer our questions.

A few weeks later, after contacting one of the names suggested by the receptionist we hit "pay dirt" so we returned for a tour. We learned that the Thomas Lockwood family had owned the mansion until 1950. Mrs. Lockwood sold the home to the Catholic Diocese of Buffalo. My eyes had picked out the right building across the street from the yoga class. Could it have been Karma or the ghosts?

We started on the tour of this lovely, stately building with a bit of humor, especially when we passed the confessional and felt that our sins were still floating in the air around it. Serious transgressions such as laughing at instructors, necking with our boyfriends, and taking pop out of machines without pay must have been a bit of comical relief for the priest. As in many historical sites, pictures of the significant family were posted in the large wood paneled library, which was out of bounds most of the time when we were there on retreat. It would probably have been a great place for capers.

We remembered our rooms with a bit of trepidation, especially Moe who had hit her head on the statue of St. Jude that Mumme had placed in her bed. The basement was off limits for retreat-ants, because this was where the staff lived. I figured that some of that staff might be in the newer colony of ghosts. The dining room had not changed except the record machine had been removed which was a good thing because Mumme might have the irresistible urge to "fix" it again.

We talked about Sister Rita and wondered if she were still alive today. It was difficult for us to decide how old Sister Rita was when we made our retreat because nuns always seemed to stay the same age due to their internal and external habits. We did know for a certainty that Sister had aged from the time the bus pulled up with us on board so many years ago until the time we left her in peace—or pieces.

Back to Where We Began

Mumme, Moe and I decided to take an excursion to South Buffalo to research our former lives at Mercy Hospital School of Nursing. Driving down Abbott Road, the large brick edifice appeared on the horizon. It felt different now. I no longer felt like Jonah headed for the belly of the whale. I recognized Mercy for what it was, a hospital, a place of learning, and a place of healing.

The Marian Hall dorm looked the same from the outside. As we entered the building, I looked toward Sister Mary Ethel's office and still expected to see her sitting there. Our former mailboxes remained in place and for a brief moment, in a sudden flashback, I looked to my spot to see if there was any mail.

It didn't feel like home. It did feel familiar and certain places like the classroom and the phone booth areas brought back a bit of nostalgia, but like so many times from the past, it is the memories of the people that fill a building. Mercy Hospital School of Nursing no longer existed. It was now Trocaire College and the nursing program had a two-year curriculum. I didn't regret those three years, but I knew that, fortunately, I had moved beyond them.

We had changed over the years since we entered this solemn arena. As student nurses, we found the place was too sedate and the silence was deafening and so we set out to make it party time. Now after fifty years of parties, we longed for the quiet meditative peace.

Reunions and Times Shared

We were gathering in a hotel in Niagara Falls for our forty-fifth reunion. The planning committee put all of the details in place and waited to see if it would all work. Several had camped out in the lobby to greet each new attendee as they entered. The shrieks of this group of older women could have rivaled any teenagers at a rock concert. Thankfully, the people behind the hotel desk seemed to be enjoying the scene.

Once in a while as another woman entered the hotel, we asked each other if this was a former classmate. We could usually figure out who they were or we would proceed to greet a person who vehemently denied ever knowing us.

After forty-five years, many had dealt with the deaths of husbands or children and some had faced life-challenging illnesses. Some of our Mercy sisterhood had gone on to heaven.

It was a time to abandon ourselves to humor and we did just that. Today was a day for wearing a happy face, reminiscing and catching up on each other's lives and finding out the paths where Mercy had led us in our nursing careers.

Kathy M. had brought along her scrapbooks to share. She had carefully organized these reminders of our past. As each of us pondered these mementos, we were reminded of our former lives. The Mercy Handbook of Rules and Regulations was a cause for laughter as we imagined the students of today living under those restrictions. Everything was spelled out on those printed pages. If a student had any questions about behavior, this Handbook was all-inclusive with instructions for studying, behavior, infractions and punishments for infractions.

Nowhere did it cover turning up the speed of a recording on retreat or moving mattresses and statues. Obviously, these were not infractions. The reunion was a time for a lot of laughter, a few tears, and a chance to reminisce and to share our life stories.

The Memoir Begins

Over the years, there were times when I would think back to the days of the creative capers of the class of 1963, and know that they had helped us to survive. When Mumme suggested writing a memoir, I agreed, because the capers had always taken me to interesting places like the confessional or a phone booth before and I could only anticipate what adventures might be awaiting me now.

Mumme and Moe were excited because one loved history and the other loved genealogy and I figured that most of the jails these days would be somewhat comfortable, if someone came after us. They seemed to write non-stop and they filled pages. They acted like compulsive athletes on the last leg of a marathon, only this was a writing marathon. I was amazed until I remembered their creative spirits and how they could both be consumed with a project.

Mumme wrote so much that I was sure that she never slept. Moe wasn't far behind her. Mumme also sent emails about publishing that could have filled an entire section in the local library. She deserved points for persistence. I considered suggesting that she attend an over-achievers anonymous meeting.

Looking over this memoir, I realize that we were innocent and protected from the world. Infractions that were punished by campusing the offender would be laughed at today. We had survived those three years either because of the rules and restrictions, or despite them. Life has a way of leading us to interesting paths, such as the road to South Buffalo Mercy and Sister Mary Ethel, whom I now realize protected us from ourselves so we could continue on our journeys.

Photo Gallery

The Nursing Goal

Student Handbook of Rules and Regulations

Mercy Hospital

Laughing Outside Marian Hall

Marian Hall

Classroom, Marian Hall

Classroom, Marian Hall

The Student Lounge

Movie Night at Marian Hall

Endless Hospital Corridors

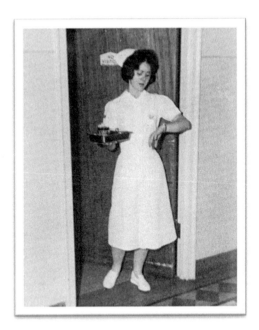

Time for Vital Signs

The Hospital Tunnel

Psychiatric Hospital

Off Duty

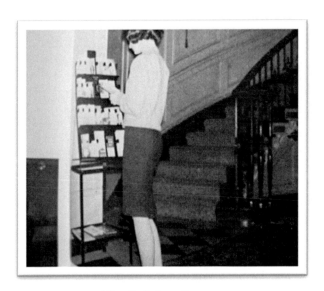

The Religious Retreat

Sister Mary Ethel

Sister Mary Claver and Sister Cyrilla

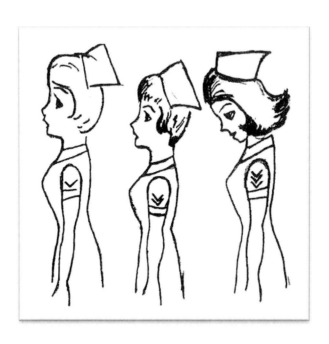

Hair Off Collar

The Bed Bath

28.5 Days Left and We Graduate

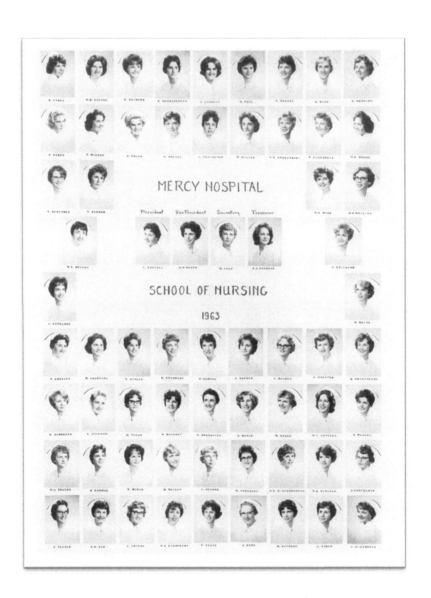

The Class of 1963

Our 40th Reunion

Mercy Girls Lunch, 2011

Section 2

Maureen Mumme Ott

I was born in Dunkirk, New York and years went by while I was looking the other way. I graduated from Mercy Hospital School of Nursing in 1963, and that road led to forty-three more years in a profession that I loved, nursing in both the United States and Canada, with the last nineteen years in public health nursing in St. Catharines, Ontario, Canada.

Today, I am a seventy-year-old woman with bad eyes and a bum knee, but with a keen interest in life, writing and the fierce enjoyment of three children and five grandchildren.

You may think, by reading the above facts, that I am a normal-sort-of-woman. That would not be true. I am exceedingly eccentric. In fact, Bob, our editor, was surprised that my writing was so sane.

I would like to thank Sister Mary Ethel, Director of Nursing at Mercy Hospital School of Nursing for "getting my back up" in 1960. I was never the same—and neither was she.

Chapter One

We Arrive

(September 6, 1960)

"When you take a Path, the Path Takes You" (Irish Saying)

When I look back on my nursing school years from the safety and wisdom of my senior years, I wonder how I survived it at all. But survive it I did, and went on to have a forty-three-year career in nursing. Sister Mary Ethel our Director of Nursing, would not have believed it. Actually, neither can I.

At seventeen, I applied to nursing school, and a few months later the letter came. The return address, typed in blue ink, read "Mercy Hospital School of Nursing," and made my heart seize up.

Opening the envelope with fingers suddenly uncooperative, I scanned the invitation to a "Pre-admission Interview" with Sister Mary Ethel, Director of Nurses. A "good news" letter! The final step of the application process for nursing school! Anticipation! Elation! Fear of the unknown!

I spent the morning thinking about what to wear on my first day of nursing school. These are the thoughts of a seventeen-year old student who wears uniforms to high school; navy blue surge, itchy, rough fabric things with white collars and cuffs. It was good to dream of real clothes worn with style; maybe a plaid skirt, cardigan sweater set and bobby socks...a circle pin could complete the outfit!

I had no thought at the time as to how soon I would be in another kind of uniform—starched white cotton dress of modest below-the-knee length, white stockings, white shoes, and white cap.

Graduating from high school that June, I started nurses training three months later. It would be a long three years; three years of Sister Mary Ethel. We were to be each other's nemeses. It would be three years of roller coaster instruction, commandments and clinical curiosities, but I did not know that yet. It would be three years of friendships with dear classmates, friendships that would last forever. But I did not know that yet either.

So, on a spring day in the suburbs of Western New York, the mailman delivered a letter and changed my life in ways I never could have imagined.

Some might have said, "Why, she was fine when she left here..."

I Think I Want to Be a Nurse

I was ten years old in 1952 when I decided to become a nurse. Mother wanted me to be an elementary school teacher, but I guess I preferred blood and viruses to loud little people.

My first thoughts of nursing began around the time my sister Mary and I visited Aunt Agnes for the summer in the small town of Litchfield, Illinois. Aunt Agnes, a Chief Warrant Officer in the Women's Army Corps, lived in a small house with a front porch where we spent a lot of time. Mary and I learned how to play poker, speak "Alfalfa" language, and—huddled under blankets on the front porch glider—not be afraid of lightning during a storm.

One day Aunt Agnes decided to take us for ice cream, but we did not get very far. As she backed her black 1950 Packard Custom 8 out of the driveway, Mary fell out of the car. The car door was not shut tightly, and Mary tumbled out onto the cinder driveway, screaming, her knee scraped and bleeding.

So instead of going for ice cream, we went for stitches at Dr. Powell's office.

In the doctor's examining room, I said: "Dr. Powell, I'll be a nurse when I grow up. So I'll help you pick cinders out of my sister's knee.

"As you wish, dear," the doctor said, "just sit there on that stool."

"Yes, Doctor," I said proudly, sitting on a low, revolving stool near Mary.

The doctor began by cleansing the wound, then, using hemostats, he began removing the gravel pieces embedded in Mary's knee. Soon the blood flowed. Mary screamed. I fainted and slumped to the floor. Now the physician had two patients.

I came to with the help of smelling salts, and vaguely heard the doctor's words, that if I wanted to have a career in nursing, it would be really helpful to stay conscious and on my feet during a medical procedure.

So my first wound care was a dismal failure. I would really need to improve in the years ahead.

I Still Want to Be a Nurse

My desire to enter nursing school was intensified the year my mother became ill. She was young, forty-five years old, and died in 1955. Some things in life are unfair and tragic. That was one of them.

I was twelve at the time and helped care for her before she was hospitalized. Mother had cut her finger on a rose thorn while gardening, and then developed an infection that needed warm soaks of Epsom salt three times a day.

Because I was *going to be a nurse*, I took on that task with loving eagerness, sure that my care and ability to follow doctor's orders to the "T" would save her. Afternoons after school and at bedtime, I would pull out the old navy blue enameled roasting pan, pitted and dented from years of use. I would fill it with the warm mixture and carry it up to Mother's bedroom.

She would be propped up on pillows, under the blue plaid quilt on the mahogany four-poster bed with the pineapples carved on top, often reading a favorite book, but sometimes sleeping. I would ensure that her reddened, painful hand was soaked for the required twenty minutes, and then bandaged.

I find it hard to recall today what she looked like back then. I think I see her in my memory, but it may simply be from old photographs, curled with age, kept in a bedroom closet in a blue shoebox. She had red curly hair, a wicked Irish wit, and lots of freckles. A devoted Irish Catholic, she never missed mass and ensured that her four children and husband attended as well.

The infection in her finger soon became blood poisoning and she was admitted to Millard Fillmore Hospital, where she died shortly thereafter. I could not believe that my nursing care did not save her. I remember walking for hours after being told of her death, feelings of shock, numbness and guilt swirling around me, thinking, *Maybe the soaks weren't warm enough...maybe I didn't time them right.*

I learned then that sometimes all the nursing care in the world is not enough to cure your patient. It was an early nursing lesson I never forgot. It was a heavy lesson for a twelve-year-old girl.

Was I Cut Out for Nursing?

Well, in career hindsight, perhaps I should have owned a bookstore instead of owning a nursing life. Imagine sitting in a soft chair, a soft light glowing over your shoulder and reading for hours! Delightful!

There's a certain dichotomy in me; sometimes a loner, yet sometimes happy to be with people. But if I'm with people too much and too long, I need to retreat, be by myself and recuperate for a while—almost like I need to recharge my batteries, get re-energized.

I also seem to be a bit quirky, with a strong streak of eccentricity. Future nursing material? Maybe, maybe not...time would tell.

Sister Mary Ethel

My father drove me to South Buffalo for my interview with Sister Mary Ethel. It was a warm spring day and the windows were open on the 1949 Ford Woodie-Wagon. It was a good thing, too, because the breezes helped counteract the exhaust fumes that came up from the hole in the floorboard in the back seat. I used to love watching the road fly by as we drove, but today I sat in the front seat, thoughts filled with nursing school.

Dad made the trip from Kenmore to South Buffalo in about forty minutes, and then cruised along Abbot Road to Choate Avenue. He eased the wagon to a stop in front of Marian Hall; the nurses' residence that I hoped would soon become my home for three years.

"I'll let you off," he said, "then go find a place to park. I'll meet you inside, Maureen. But before you go in, I want to tell you something. I am very proud of you and I just know you'll be accepted today. You'll be just like your Aunt Jane, your mother's sister," he told me. "She went to Mercy Hospital as well; back in 1942, I think. She went there at least for a few years...got appendicitis, they operated on her at Mercy, she died...something to do with the anesthesia, so they said."

Hearing of a dead nursing student relative did not really help me have a lot of confidence. I was worried about meeting Sister Mary Ethel; worried about a future in nursing school. I was feeling anxious, a regular teeter-totter of emotions and doubts.

Could I really be a nurse? What if I killed somebody one day by accident? Gave the wrong medicine? Dropped a slippery baby on its little head? Forgot to put the side rail up...patient falls out of bed, breaks a leg, gets pneumonia and dies? Nurse fired from job! And what comical lunacy makes me consider three more years of nuns after four years of high school nuns? Like walking off the edge of a cliff because I had a death wish.

But I was soon sitting in a small office, and heard a swish of rosary beads announce the Director's presence.

"You may call me Sister Mary Ethel," the nun said, sitting at her desk. "I am the Director here, and if you are accepted into the program, I will be responsible for your nursing education. Now tell me, why do you want to be a nurse, Miss Mumme?"

She was a big woman with beady eyes, solidly built and poured tightly into a snowy white habit. She made me uneasy. I had the feeling she could read my mind, a place I liked to keep hidden from prying eyes.

I stuttered my carefully planned answer, "I want to care for sick people and ease their suffering. I also think it's good preparation for marriage and a family in the future."

I couldn't tell her that five of my high school classmates had applied to Mercy as well, and it seemed to me that I might as well go there, too.

Sister smiled as if my answer had pleased her.

I did not mention personality traits that could hinder my goal of a nursing career. Like being a bit of a prankster, a tendency to daydream, and a crying need for long stretches of space and solitude, something at odds with nursing school life.

Well, somehow the interview went well and shortly thereafter I was accepted into Mercy Hospital School of Nursing. My dream had come true, but there were some nightmares ahead.

I Become a Mercy Girl

It was September 6, 1960; I would soon be eighteen when I and sixty-five other Mercy Girls moved our belongings into Marian Hall. The school was located in an Irish-American, working-class neighborhood of South Buffalo, New York. Steel mills, foundries and other industries provided employment for the residents of this mostly middle class neighborhood.

All student nurses lived in Marian Hall, a tall, four-story L-shaped building, with a long paved path leading up to two large double doors that clicked with a final "now we've got you!" sound when they closed. Doors were locked at night to keep us "safely" inside and to keep any boyfriends out.

The building was actually well designed, with appealing checkerboard-patterned brickwork and a curved archway over the front doors. The dorm was attached to the massive Mercy Hospital via a creepy underground tunnel.

I remember that dorm so well, the simple utilitarian blandness of it, the small student rooms and trying to brighten things up by decorating with bright bedspreads and matching drapes. I recall with fondness the smell of toast and peanut butter in the dorm lounge, and drinking chocolate milk after a difficult shift on a hospital ward.

When you entered Marian Hall you saw them immediately—the Housemothers!

A Housemother, who is the representative of the Director of the School, is in attendance in Marian Hall and is responsible for the conduct of the residence. (Student Handbook)

Yes, the Housemothers, the eyes and ears of Marian Hall. *Loud conversations and shouting in the corridors and rooms are to be avoided (Student Handbook).* "Girls, stop that noise right this minute!" How often would we hear that over the loudspeaker during the next three years!

Our Housemothers resided in an office near the entrance, an office elevated for a better view and vantage point (theirs, not ours). If you did not see them, you felt their eyes on you as you signed in and out. "Signing in" was mandatory when you entered or left the dorm. Those Housemothers were everywhere and missed very little.

And the evening's indignity? Bed check. At approximately eleven p.m. your dorm room door was opened suddenly, a bright light shown in on your "sleeping" body curled up in a small metal bed, then the door shut quietly but firmly and the footsteps receded, only to torment the student in the next room, and the next and the next, until all were accounted for that night. Florence Nightingale had her lamp; the Housemother had her flashlight.

What was so hard for me was living in a Marian Hall-world where my life was so rigidly controlled and monitored by nuns and Housemothers. Dorm life for me would be a constant struggle between following the rules and rebellion. It could be said that because most things were illegal or forbidden at Mercy Hospital School of Nursing, breaking the law (without getting caught and punished) became my student mantra.

The Nuns: A Habit I Learned to Avoid

Ah, the Sisters of Mercy...they may be long gone from our lives, but never forgotten. Sometimes we thought they were an instrument of mercy, at other times we prayed for a mercy killing.

They originated from a congregation of women in Dublin, Ireland in 1827 whose founder was Irishwoman Catherine Elizabeth McAuley, the eldest in an ancient and distinguished family. She opened the first House of Mercy, a shelter to educate and feed young women and girls.

So it's Catherine we have to thank for three years of nun's control and our feeble attempts at nun-conformity (for me, it was non-conformity). Three years of dormitory living, with the sisters guiding their nursing student charges with zeal and energy; years that would change us forever, bonding us to each other in ways that never would have occurred if these women had not been watching our every move. It was the Mercy Girls against the Mercy Sisters, and the battle lasted for three years (for me, perhaps a bit longer).

Each nun was encased in a billowing habit as white as homogenized milk, with a stiffly starched headpiece. On their chests they wore breastplate-like things that perched there like huge white Necco Wafers. Back then I thought these devices were worn so nuns could pretend that they had no bosoms.

A wimple, an elaborately starched cloth worn around their head, imprisoned their faces. It made their pinched skin look like corrugated hospital-white vinyl siding.

Sensible black shoes completed the outfit. The only visible skin consisted of scrunched-up faces and hands.

The ultimate effect of the habit was one of a large white swishing presence, with eyes that watched, like a cat waiting for the mouse. Although we all knew that they had feet under that garb, those nuns never made a sound—they moved silently and in stealth, happy to sneak up on hapless student nurses and catch them in some misdemeanor.

This I had to watch out for—like avoiding a bacillus or a virus. I felt targeted by the good sisters and with some valid reasons. Ours was not to become a style of open rebellion in school, but rather organized and subtle maneuvers of impish pranks and games. We targeted the powerful nuns and each other, in harmless but often brilliant fun, or so we thought at the time.

Chapter Two

We Begin

(Freshman Year)

We Become Alphabetized and Meet Sister Mary Claver

I remember it all too well—the start of freshman year. We were gathered in the large basement classroom of Marian Hall. It was an October morning, crisp and cold outside, but warm inside the dorm.

A tall, thin nun introduced herself as Sister Mary Claver, and told us she would be our nursing instructor for the Fundamentals of Nursing class. A rabbit-like woman with a beaked nose and shy, kind smile, Sister spoke briskly but in absent-minded, run-on sentences. She reminded me a bit of Mr. Magoo, that 1960s cartoon character, with similar mannerisms.

We nicknamed her "Beaver" for her buck-toothed grin, and soon we forgot she had a formal name. We soon learned that Beaver also had difficulty with names.

If you had a one syllable last name, Sister could pronounce it easily. But if you were unfortunate enough to have a longer last name, then your name got muddled and mutilated.

Example: Calling on Miss Mary Wintermantel became, "Miss Wintermint...Winter...um...Wintermute...no...Miss Withermantel...no...oh, never mind, you up there, just answer my question." See? Mr. Magoo in a nun's habit.

I was seated in one of the room's many combination desk/chairs, a 1940s oak contraption consisting of a narrow wooden chair with a top writing surface/armrest attached. These desks required a nimbleness of body and agility in order to seat yourself and avoid hitting your shins on the writing part; you had to slide sideways into your seat in a smooth, quick motion while bending the knees until you landed on the seat. If that kind of motion made a sound, it would be, "swish/flop."

Seating was arranged in a tiered fashion of rows, with a large teaching area in front, holding a few hospital beds, a dummy patient (Mrs. Chase, quiet but useful) and various medical paraphernalia. It would become our "practice area" for basic nursing functions like blood pressures, bed-making, giving needles, enemas, and intravenous therapy. It would also give us many hours of merry adventure with our beloved Beaver.

Beaver strode back and forth in front of her young students, and began roll call. As directed, we called out our last names loudly, in alphabetical order. We also had to sit in alphabetical order.

In addition to being sorted out alphabetically, our class was further divided into two distinct groups, the "A" group (last names starting with "A" and ending with the first "M"s) and the "B" group (finishing off the "M"s and rolling on to the "Z"s). The A and B groups became so used to sounding off last names, that it became a soothing rhythmic cadence for us and a few of us can reel off those names to this day, almost fifty years later (ask Mary, of the B group).

Today it makes me wonder, what if we'd had a student back then with a hyphenated last name? Not likely in the 60s, but it could have happened. Would Kimberly Brown-Reynolds sit with the A group (Brown)? The B group (Reynolds)? Would she be torn between groups? Alphabet soup, that's for sure. It just makes me smile.

If I could fold back time and years, I would like to sit once again in Beaver's class and watch with relish as she dealt with the alphabetizing of a hyphenated student name. And I would take notes.

The Beaver and Her Bloopers

One morning in class, Beaver began the day's instruction on hospital bed making, stressing how a well-made bed ensured the patient's well-being. The bottom sheet needed to be tight enough that a quarter bounced when tossed on the bed (no fitted sheets in the 60s); and if it did not, the bed would be torn apart and made all over again.

"Tighter now, girls, or you'll have bedsores," urged Beaver. "Now stop your hilarity, will you just this once?" the dear nun asked.

I had been bored during class, distracted and thinking my own far-away thoughts, watching the bed-making efforts of some of my classmates without really watching. I had grasped the concept, so felt I could move on to more interesting things in my head. Only my eyes were watching Sister, my mind was not.

Sister's voice in front of me ebbed away, and then suddenly came into sharper focus.

What was that? What did she just say?

"Now girls," the nun had said, "if this patient can assist me to ensure that he is not left in the bed when we are all through..."

I smiled, listening carefully as Beaver instructed us in the art of bed making without trapping the patient between the sheets.

"Things move around here when you least expect it...now girls, look, see and observe..."

Beaver carried on; oblivious of the effect her words were having on me as I sat up straight, suddenly alert and paying rapt attention.

I could feel a slow grin happening. My God, I thought, Beaver is so funny if you listen to her words; take them at face value and their exact meaning! The nun had no idea, but she was a Jack Benny, a Jackie Gleason, and a Lucille Ball all dressed up in a white habit! She was Harvey, the white rabbit!

I grabbed my pen and wrote down verbatim the words that Beaver had just uttered. I nudged Sis M. sitting next to me to show her what I had written, then swung my head towards Beaver, indicating the author. Sis tried not to laugh out loud.

"Show the girls in the lounge on break-time!" she said.

I noticed then that Sis was now paying rather close attention to Beaver, listening as I was in a totally new way. An idea had been born.

Sister continued her work, with a "huff" and a grunt to pull a draw sheet tight on the bed.

"Do you see what I mean, girls? Well then, stand! You there, Miss Zabook, err, Zellward, come and try this."

I listened intently during the remainder of the class, as well as future classes as Beaver's nursing instructions went on; how to make a hospital bed, give an enema, a shot, take a temperature, and on and on.

Beaver continued to be "the pun–nun," and I continued to write furiously, head bent in concentration; writing hand moving fast to capture each word. Beaver's funny phrases were recorded forever, our beloved "Beaver's Bloopers," to be reviewed and enjoyed after class each day in the student lounge, and for years to come.

Here are a few of my favorites:

> "If this patient can assist me in getting on the bedpan..."

> "And at that time, you can tie the visitor up."

> "You'll find most patients with throat conditions breathe..."

> "Girls, be very observant and watch, and you too can get into the medicine."

> "When you draw the line on the buttocks, you are not making a blessing."

> "If you are going to be attentive to a patient, make it a patient with feelings."

"Miss Winter...um...Wintermute...what are you enjoying up there so much in your chair...can't you pay attention and take notes like Miss Mumme?"

I was taking notes all right, Beaver's Bloopers notes, a blog-like history of inane utterances that would make us all laugh for years after we graduated, notes that would be read at reunions, notes that were to become a treasured part of our student nursing experience.

After some time, we would take turns capturing her bloopers in class, sharing them afterwards with great relish. Sister Beaver thought we were the most attentive, studious, note-taking class she ever had.

Well, We *Look* Like Nurses...

We never told anyone but each other that we had no idea what we were doing in that first year of nurses training. But we were happy to wear the simple white nursing uniform and act the part. At least we *looked* like nurses, even though we didn't know a catheter from an enema tube in those days. There was not much about the uniform that was functional or constructive. Stiff, board-like things...I felt like a marionette wearing it.

The uniforms were washed and starched by the hospital laundry; rigid as a bed board, the thing would stand all by itself on the floor...nobody in it, just a dress missing a student. The starched collar scratched my neck, leaving angry red marks, like a teacher's comments scrawled upon a failing term paper.

But never mind that, I thought, I was starting to be a nurse. I looked like a nurse, so it must be so.

The Hospital Tunnel

It was a morning in December, a snowy day, which in South Buffalo, could quickly turn into a blizzard-like, overwhelming deluge of snow. We had been in nursing school a grand total of four months. Sister Cyrilla had scheduled ten of us for a tour on "how to navigate the hospital tunnel."

A long, torturous tube, the hospital tunnel connected Marian Hall to the basement bowels of the hospital—a real convenience to save time and frostbite during South Buffalo winters.

The tunnel would save us from being outside in nasty storms. Also, if I went outside in Buffalo's deep snow, I might disappear in a flurry of white uniform, blending with the stuff, never to be seen again.

The *Student Handbook* made reference to the *Rules of the Tunnel* (page 11):

> All students are to use the hospital CENTER STAIRS when going to or from the hospital basement. It is strongly recommended that students do not use the tunnel when alone going to or from the hospital (an obvious legal disclaimer, as we were almost always alone going to our afternoon or night shifts.) When using the tunnel after 10:30 P.M. the Housemother is to be notified by phone from the hospital Information Desk that you are coming. She will then be at the door to meet you (we hoped).

Sister Cyrilla swished off in front of us, saying firmly, "Now girls, follow me," and we followed, down three steps off the main dorm hallway.

She was a teacher of "biological sciences," but I can't recall a word she taught. She was shrewd, with steady brown eyes behind wire-rimmed glasses. She struggled to open the heavy tunnel door. We rushed to assist her and followed like baby ducklings as she walked down another three steps, until we were in the tunnel.

"Now, girls, follow me and pay close attention," she said, looking at us with intense eyes that said, "Pay attention or something bad could happen to you!"

She continued, "Yes, pay close attention. You don't ever want to get lost down here. You could be wandering down here for a month of Sundays, with only the Good Lord knowing you are missing!"

This did not sound like a good idea to me, so I paid close attention.

It was only a four-minute tunnel walk between the dorm and the hospital, but it seemed to take a lot longer. We took four turns through that winding, humid, womb-like place before we reached the door to the hospital. There were no signs to guide us, so we had to rely on memory alone.

"Why, it's like being in a cave," I said to Sister, "only there are no stalactites or stalagmites!"

"We'll have none of your humor here today, Miss Mumme, save it for the lounge," and Sister continued on, intent on getting us oriented and unafraid.

That tunnel always gave me anxious moments...it's a place that never leaves your memory. The walls were painted a straw yellow, (the color of the urine samples we would soon be collecting from our patients) and were lined with huge white pipes hissing and spitting steam.

I was always afraid one might burst and scald me to death before I graduated. The smell down there reminded me of a basket of wet laundry before being hung out on the line—no, more like the smell of a Laundromat—warm, moist heat with the pipes hissing like irons attacking damp shirts.

In my young, vivid imagination, I had fears of being in that tunnel alone. What if I was heading back from an evening shift and met a man down there? He could be hiding around a corner and grab me. I could be raped in two minutes flat and no one would save me. It could all be over before I could reach a phone to notify the Housemother.

I would be ruined for marriage. As good Catholic girls, we really tried to keep our virginity in those days (some of us trying harder than others). I imagined the man in grubby, unwashed clothes smelling of sweat and dirt. He would have beady, evil eyes that would terrorize me, like an owl watching its mouse victim.

Or I could take a wrong turn and get lost, then be late for my shift. Being late was a mortal sin. Why think of the embarrassment of classmates learning you forgot how to navigate the meanderings of the tunnel. Getting lost was something I was really good at.

I knew that I was not alone in thinking of that tunnel as an uneasy place to be...like being in a doctor's waiting room, fearing you were pregnant—it was that type of uneasy, anxious, dreading place.

Nothing bad ever happened to me in the hospital tunnel, but the thought of potential disaster always made me scurry from one end to the other, looking behind me for predators.

The hospital tunnel is still in use today and, having visited it recently, I can tell you that it still is a ghoulish god-awful pit of a place.

Weekends Away

We attended classes at Canisius College that first year, but lived for weekends off. They were our Rice Krispies of living, the snap, crackle, and pop that made our three-year school experience bearable. We could go home if we lived nearby. Or, better yet, with permission we could go home with a classmate.

If you were unlucky enough to be staying in the dorm over the weekend, you had "weekend" rules:

- Sign in and out under the scrutiny of Housemother
- Curfews, one for Friday and one for Saturday night
- Dress codes to observe
- Nuns watching and interviewing our dates (if we had any)

Consensus was: Weekends in Marian Hall were hell.

Most of us went home for our two-day escape, but the very best fun was "weekends away with our friends." Glory Alleluia and Yippee Yahoo! The solution to restrictions, the salt of life, the balm that soothes, and the drink that refreshes! With our parent's permission, we could go home with a classmate for two fabulous days, returning by ten p.m. on Sunday.

Friday and Saturday night partying at a local bar, meeting friends or relatives of our classmates, being in a different city, oh, it was glorious! We forgot all about fevers and saline solutions, fleet enemas, saphenous veins, and sebaceous glands. Together, we often woke up with simultaneous hangovers.

On more than one occasion I went home to Rochester with my friend, Linda Z. (the last student of the B group). Linda had a raucous laugh, unflinchingly honest gaze, and an independent spirit.

On Friday nights, we went to a local Rochester bar. We drank beer and danced, met new guys, drank more beer and danced some more.

One weekend, I recall Linda parking her parent's car off to the side of a local road. We had a plan. To meet guys. We struggled to put the hood up, pretending there was something wrong with the engine. Then we waited. It always worked. We met a few really nice guys that way, but nothing ever came of it.

We usually got home from our partying around two in the morning, tipsy with drink and fatigue and laughter, falling into our beds and asleep in minutes.

The morning light always woke me—or was it the "hangover thirst?" Cobwebs for brains, I longed for orange juice to quench my thirst and raise my blood sugar. Minutes later, Linda's mother appeared, as if she had overheard my silent plea, with a large cold glass of orange juice to sip in bed. I really liked the pampering at Linda's house and adored her gentle parents.

When Linda went home with me, the same pattern continued, except for the absence of pampering. No orange juice in bed. Dad was more likely to offer Linda a shot of Jim Beam or Four Roses bourbon. Being one of five children did not get you a whole lot of consideration at my house. Linda and I would go out to the Jolly Inn or Sully's Bar, meet boys, dance, drink and party. Oh, weekends away from Mercy were *a very good time.*

Memories of Rochester with Linda will be with me forever. Being at Linda's house felt like a velvet blanket, the kind with the satin hem that soothes your fingers and your senses when you stroke it.

Almost fifty years later, Linda and I still get together for "weekends," even though we live more than a hundred miles apart. Dorothy Parker said it best in describing this lifelong relationship: "Constant use had not worn ragged the fabric of their friendship."

Getting Campused

The term, "getting campused" was the punishment for moderately serious infractions of the *Mercy Hospital School of Nursing Student Handbook.* Misconduct was not to be tolerated. Missing curfew (ten-thirty p.m. on weeknights; midnight on weekends) or loud yelling in the dorm could land a student in front of Sister Mary Ethel for a disciplinary meeting. I speak to you of this from experience. "Getting campused" was followed, as night follows day, by restrictions on freedom of movement (no going home on weekends, no going out for a beer in the evening).

I was often under "house arrest" in the dorm, the result of an invitation to visit with Sister Mary Ethel. Her office was a smallish room on the first floor with grey-blue walls and a large double hung window draped with garish chintz curtains. In the corner was a statue of the Virgin Mary, perched atop a doily-draped wooden pedestal. Her holy hands folded calmly in prayer, I was sure she was pulling for me to make it through.

Sister sat in front of the window, the light casting a bright halo around her, giving a student the impression that she was a larger-than-life power figure. Staring at you behind large rimless spectacles, she caused fear in many a misbehaving student.

I probably hold the record for most student infractions in my three years of nursing study. Sister often stressed the three most important aspects of living, which must be considered in order for a student nurse to "realize her vocation" in life, and she never neglected to share them with me.

One day, I was invited to stop by her office, and with heavy heart sat in front of her on a hard metal office chair.

"Miss Mumme, you missed bed check last night." Sister's beady eyes probed my very being.

"Sister, all I did was I forgot to sign in when I got back from Mischler's. Then I was in the bathroom, I guess, when the Housemother did bed check."

Lame truth, but truth nevertheless.

"Miss Mumme," Sister sighed, "I have no evidence to support your version of events. Now, the nursing student must see herself first as a religious person, secondly as a professional person, and finally as a social person. You, however, seem to have these priorities mixed up. You see yourself first as a social person. Your priorities need adjusting. Curfew is curfew and you need to remember to sign the Attendance Book when you return from an outing. And you need to be in your bed at bed check time. A professional person would ensure this. You try my patience more than any other student here."

There was no sense arguing my case. I had no evidence.

"Yes, Sister, sorry, Sister." I said, agreeing with my mouth, but not my attitude.

"It seems to me, Miss Mumme, that your behavior at times is not becoming of a Mercy student and a future professional nurse."

"Yes, Sister, I can change that."

The nun sighed, fingering the pencil on her desk, "Confession is good for the soul. You might want to see Father this weekend and ask forgiveness."

"But my soul didn't do anything, Sister," I blurted out without thinking things through.

I felt the glaring eyes staring hard at me and I looked down into my lap.

"Campused this weekend, Miss Mumme. Take this note to the Housemother. Being here this weekend will give you ample time for reflection."

Well, never mind, she had me again...it was no use explaining.

"Thank you, Sister."

Standing up for myself only got me into more trouble, so I just stood up and left.

"Mr. Bailey, Time for your Temperature, Sir..."

After practicing the proper technique for taking a patient's temperature on our classroom dummy patient, Mrs. Chase, I soon was ready for the real thing on the hospital wards.

I began supervised hospital duty later in that first year of training. Patient contact initially consisted of simple procedures like temperatures and blood pressure readings, studying patient charts, looking up drugs in the *Physician's Desk Reference* and consulting frequently with my nursing instructors.

One Monday morning, I was assigned to Miss Gottstine, one of the best student instructors on the Medical ward. Miss Gottstine was a small, intense woman with short brown curly hair and eyes that followed your every move and missed nothing.

She was stern, but kind, and seemed to know how really inept students felt at performing any task that first year.

I felt sweat on my brow and hands when Miss Gottstine ordered, "Miss Mumme, please go down to Mr. Bailey's (name changed to protect his privacy) room and take his temperature.

As he has been running a fever, of course his is to be a rectal temperature."

Earlier that day I had taken a rectal temperature on a female patient, but now would be faced with my first rectal on a male bottom. The thought embarrassed and appalled me. I felt my face beginning to flush before I even reached Mr. Bailey's room.

Following correct procedure, I carried a little white enamel tray, reviewing its contents to make sure I had everything: glass thermometer lying on a gauze square, lubricant, and a little card with the patient's name and room number. Check. I had forgotten nothing.

With great bravado, I entered the room and said quickly, "Good morning, Mr. Bailey, it's time for your rectal temperature. Let me just check your wrist band to identify you. Thanks so much...and now can you please turn on your side?

"Why, sure, nurse," murmured my patient.

So far, so good. *This will be a breeze*, I thought.

The man obediently turned on his side away from me and lay there silently. I greased the thermometer with the lubricant, turned his bed covers down and approached his buttocks.

Slippery device in hand, I aimed, and then stopped. I stared in utter surprise. A large scrotum was hanging down between his buttocks, blocking his anal opening from view and me from completing my nursing task. How could I get the thermometer in with his scrotum in the way? I pulled my hand back with a jerk, but I could not pull my gaze away from that wrinkled sack nestled between the twin globes of his bottom.

"What to do, what to do," I muttered half out loud, my lips pursed and brow furrowed, thinking...

Do I move the thing aside myself? Do I say anything when I move it? Am I even supposed to move it? Or do I politely ask him to move it? And if I do ask him to move it, how do I ask politely? Do I say:

"Mr. Bailey, can you please move your scrotum forward?" No, that sounded awfully awkward.

"Mr. Bailey, can you please reposition your testicles to in front of your legs?" No, worse!

"Mr. Bailey, your privates are in the way and are blocking your rectum." Nope, not right either.

There simply was no proper way to request the realignment of Mr. Bailey's genitals. I was flummoxed. I was embarrassed. I wanted to laugh—no—I wanted to cry.

I glanced up towards Mr. Bailey's head, wondering if he was aware of the procedural delay, but he seemed to either be sleeping or a very "patient" patient, as he did not say a word, nor did he move.

I tried quickly to review my Fundamentals of Nursing textbook, the part about rectal temperatures. I could recall no mention of what to do in cases of anal awkwardness.

Suddenly it came to me, *Get out and get some help!*

I said brightly, "I'll be right back, Mr. Bailey, I think my instructor is calling me," (beautiful ruse!) and I left the room to find Miss Gottstine.

I was not sure how to explain my predicament to her, but decided to use as many proper medical words as professionally possible (it would make me look good in her eyes).

"Miss Gottstine, can you please help me with Mr. Bailey's rectal temperature?" I whispered to her outside the patient's room, "His scrotum is blocking my approach to his anus."

Miss Gottstine's eyes widened in surprise, her nostrils flared and her lips pursed. I thought for a minute that she was trying not to laugh.

"Hmm, I see, come with me dear, and let's see what we can do."

In the patient's room again, we approached the bed and once again I announced the rectal temperature procedure to Mr. Bailey. He was still on his side facing away from us.

"Hmm, sure, nurse," he murmured, seemingly half asleep. My instructor pulled the bed cover away and quickly moving the offending testicles aside a bit, inserted the temperature with skill and ease.

"OH, I see!" I said.

"See?" said Miss Gottstine.

"Yes, I do see!" I said, my voice relieved and grateful.

Looking at my silver metal nurse's watch with the second hand, I began to time the procedure. The rest of the task went off without a hitch.

Textbook situations are rarely textbook realities for student nurses. All options need to be considered if one wants to be a technically competent nurse one day. I speak to you of this with hands-on experience.

Giving Shots

Sister Mary Claver was my favorite instructor. The Beaver taught us how to give a shot...in her own unique way. We practiced on oranges in the basement classroom, but first Beaver demonstrated and taught the injection procedure.

There she was, in front of her large oak desk, a tall, thin envelope of white. Beside her on the desk was a tray with a glass hypodermic syringe, a stoppered vial of clear liquid, a tin of cotton balls, and a small bottle of alcohol.

"Now girls," she said, "in the beginning, you're going to have a lot of thumbs when you inject the patient." (I made a note, giggling silently.) She then explained the process and the difference between an intramuscular and subcutaneous shot (one went into the muscle and the other went into the tissue just under the skin). "But first, girls, you must always remember to cleanse the skin with alcohol. Take your dossil (cotton ball), dab it with your alcohol. Now spread the dossil around in a circular motor..." (I wrote this down, smiling.)

Well, the class was in a quiet fit of laughter over her words. We tried valiantly not to show our amusement and muffled what guffaws we could. But at the same time, we were very interested in the subject of shots and anxious to learn, practice, and then give shots to our patients. It was a clinical task that we relished, a concrete act that said, "yes, you are indeed a nurse...look what you can do!"

Beaver continued, using Mrs. Chase, our class mannequin as a patient.

"Now girls, here's our Mrs. Chase, waiting for us. I'll just turn her over into position for an injection into her buttocks. Remember to always check the patient's armband for proper identification, or you could be very surprised one day by a medication error!" Sister then pulled down Miss Bedford's pajama bottom, exclaiming, "To give a shot in the buttocks, bring their pajama tops down." (Laughter all around!)

Demonstrating the location of the "upper outer quadrant" of the buttock as the ideal injection site, Beaver used her finger to divide Miss Bedford's buttock into four imaginary quarters. "Girls, the upper, outer quadrant is the spot you need to aim for, in order to miss hitting the sciatic nerve. And girls, when you draw the line on the buttocks, remember you're not making a blessing!"

By now her student nurses completely lost any chance of retaining composure. I put my head down on my desk, laughing so hard that tears stained that day's Beaver's Bloopers.

Sis, sitting beside me (in correct alphabetical order), had her head back, making odd little *Hrmppp, Hrmppp, Hrmppp* peals of laughter.

Maureen O. had her mouth covered, her eyes wide with delight at Beaver's words.

Sister Mary Claver looked at us, disappointment in her eyes, "All right now! Attention now! Never mind for a moment!"

She went on with the lesson, urging us to "get in, get out, and distract the patient!"

Laughing, I added this one to my notes.

She explained that speed and accuracy was the key to the patient's comfort. Most of us couldn't wait to try this one out on live patients. We practiced and practiced, first on oranges and then on each other.

Beaver ended the class, telling us, "You can never give a hypodermic that's not well," meaning that your needle and syringe must always be sterile.

Well, all I can say about Beaver's lectures is that they were never sterile! They were full of flotsam and jetsam, words flying every which-way but up. God, I loved that nun and her way with words!

Chapter Three
We Continue
(Junior Year)

The Student Handbook: Telephone Calls

House Phone..................TR. 9903

Pay Phone, 2nd floor.........SO. 9473

Pay Phone, 3rd floor.........SO. 9262

Pay Phone, 4th floor.........SO. 9318

These are unlisted numbers. Try to limit the length of your calls. In consideration for the needs of all, there is a five-minute time limit on the use of the house phones. Students may not use the public phones at the hospital. Telephones may not be used after 10:30 P.M.

The pay phones were our extension to the outer world, our black metal friends. A phone booth on each floor of the dorm, a tiny womb with an oak bi-fold door that swooshed closed with a good pull on the door handle. After five minutes, the space became airless, causing you to open the door and lose any privacy.

Ah, the worn oak seat, rounded to fit your bottom. In my mind I can run my hand over its smoothness to this day; I recall its coolness when you first sat down.

Clunk! The dime drops into its slot, the number dialed, and you talked to a boy in the Canisius College dorm. Sweet memories.

Bathing Patients in an Eight-Bed Ward

One of the most common hospital assignments was bathing patients; always too many patients to be bathed in too little time. The wards in the hospital consisted of long halls with patient rooms holding anywhere from one to eight beds.

The bathrooms were at the end of the hall. Bad planning and misery for student nurses.

Here's a typical bath routine:

1. Greet patient, check ID, and explain bathing procedure
2. Gather towels, washcloths, soap, toothpaste or baking soda, lotion, powder, bath basin (2ft long x 1ft wide x 1ft deep = heavy when full!), emesis basin (for teeth brushing or denture cleaning)
3. Take bath basin down hall to bathroom; fill with warm water
4. Walk back down hall to patient's ward; try not to slosh water on floor; begin bath
5. If bath water gets cool, or dirty before finishing bath, walk down hall to get fresh, warm water again
6. Bathe only bits of patient at a time, covering and uncovering to protect patient modesty and keep patient warm
7. Bathe privates last; keep patient's parts covered at all times
8. Help patient brush teeth or clean dentures
9. Give back rub, using lotion and then powder
10. Change sheets (remove bottom sheet and put in laundry. Take used top sheet; put on bottom of mattress. Put clean draw sheet on mattress over bottom sheet. Pull tight. (Remember that bouncy quarter!) Put clean top sheet on bed and flannel blanket. A clean pillowcase completes the bed change.

11. Pause before exiting patient's room; did you leave room neat and tidy? Was patient's call bell within reach? Were the patient's side rails up, if necessary? Did you leave a fresh garbage bag taped to your patient's bedside table? (In those days, we made our own garbage bags out of old newspapers. They resembled little sailboats. I think I could still make one today.)

We learned how to make a bed with a patient in it, and out of it (this made us happier, as it was less work). If I had four or more patients to bathe, it sure passed the morning quickly.

Note: Today's hospital bath basins are minuscule plastic poor cousins of the original sturdy and large metal 60s basins. How you can competently wash a patient in three cups of water is beyond me!

Life's Ups and Downs

You will not believe it, but a whole paragraph in the *Student Handbook* is devoted to rules about the dorm elevator:

> Maximum capacity load, 10 students. (No mention of nuns and their effect on elevator capacity.)
>
> Students are to face the front of the car and be ready to depart when door opens. The elevator door is on automatic timing and when there is a delay of seconds before leaving the car the door starts to close before the car is empty. This could be the cause of an accident. Courtesy in use of elevators should be followed at all times.

These rules are not elaborated on, but I think the manual could simply say, "No horsing around, or backwards behavior...we know what you're doing!"

So, here is a true elevator story about my classmate, Yolanda, or "Yo," as we sometimes call her.

Yolanda is a small blond-haired woman with a scathing wit and irreverent attitude toward life. We had a lot in common, I think, as she seemed to see through things and declare them "Hogwash!" a lot.

We clashed sometimes, for I think we shared some traits of eccentricity, but I loved her for her quirkiness then and I love her to this day. She had some great stories to tell us and here is one of them. I have imagined what I think she might have said and thought in this situation.

One winter afternoon Yo was alone in the dorm elevator heading to the basement for a pop when the elevator suddenly jerked to a stop about midway between floors and the door opened up to expose a gray cinder block wall. "Shit!" yelled Yo in surprise as she picked herself up off the cold tile floor. "What the hell," she said out loud, "I was facing the front, following the rules and now look what happens!"

She jabbed the small alarm button repeatedly until she heard a voice say, "What is the matter?" Holy Moly, it was Sister Mary Ethel! *Damn!* thought Yolanda to herself, *of all nuns to answer, it has to be the "Big E!" She'll accuse me of some skullduggery, that's for sure!*

She looked for any escape before the Big E arrived. She noticed a foot-high space between the cinder wall and the bottom of the elevator, and wondered if she could squeeze through before Sister arrived. But, looking out she could see that she was about five feet above the floor; too high to jump and besides, before she could think further about jumping down, there was the Big E. "God," muttered Yolanda, "she is gonna have a bird!"

The "Big E" brought a wooden ladder, which she placed against the wall, ordering Yo to "squeeze through that opening, crawl down this ladder and get yourself out of there NOW!"

It was a tight squeeze but being thin, Yolanda managed to escape her elevator prison and climb down the ladder under the nun's watchful eyes.

Sister Mary Ethel silently handed the ladder to her student, shook her head, and ordered, "Maintenance room," and swished away.

After returning the ladder to the maintenance room, Yolanda returned to the basement, (she took the stairs this time) and got a 7Up from the pop machine. She went up to the lounge where she shared her elevator story with her classmates, "You'll never believe what just happened to me," she said, entertaining them as only Yo could, being a Lucille Ball kind of gal.

There Went My Patient

Soon after Yo's adventure, another elevator, (in the hospital, this time) caused me some trouble. One day in the spring of my junior year, I was on clinical duty on the Medical-Surgical ward. The head nurse asked me to take an elderly male patient, Mr. Simpson (name changed to protect his privacy), down to the X-ray Department for a chest x-ray. I was to ensure that all his charts accompany him.

Getting help with the transfer of my patient from bed to metal stretcher, I carefully strapped him in, lest he turn over and fall off the narrow cart. Gathering up six thick folders of charts, I pushed the stretcher down the long hall to the elevator at the end of the nursing station. I carefully guided the heavy trolley; the charts perched precariously between my forearm and the hard metal edge of the patient's bed on wheels. (In those days, the hospital carts were large, heavy metal contraptions with big wheels that turned stiffly, if at all.)

Heaving a sigh of relief that I had made it to the elevator, I pushed the button with one finger and waited. My patient was sound asleep and obviously no worse for wear for the sometimes wavy, awkward trolley trip down the long corridor. Soon the elevator doors opened and I put the charts on the floor outside the elevator, as there was no way to push my patient into the elevator without both my hands free.

Pushing the trolley into the elevator, I stepped back out to retrieve the tall stack of hospital records. Picking the charts up off the floor, I turned to follow my patient into the elevator, but instead I found myself staring at a closed elevator door.

I heard a faint whirring sound that signaled the elevator moving away—with my patient—and the thought occurred to me that I was most likely in a big heap of trouble.

An old patient on a stretcher found riding an elevator alone was not acceptable nursing practice, even for second year nursing students and I felt my heart throbbing with fear. I stabbed the elevator button repeatedly with damp fingers, but to no avail. No patient returned to me. He was gone and I was a goner.

God, Mumme, I thought, *You are such a total ditz!*

I slowly turned away and "head-down" dejected, walked back to find my instructor to relay the bad news. My thoughts tumbled this way and that, like a load of wash in the dryer, spinning round and round. *Now I'm in trouble, now I'm in trouble, spin, spin, spin...*

Mr. Simpson was eventually found and returned safely to his bed; no harm done to him in his solo travels. He was found riding from floor to floor by one of the nuns. Finding him alone and sleeping on his cart, she probably checked his wristband identification and took charge of securing an orderly to transport the poor man back to his room.

Later, I received a lecture from my instructor on comprehensive, safe patient care during transport. Oh, and yes, I did have to complete a Hospital Incident Report—standard hospital procedure for strange and unusual happenings. Losing a patient on an elevator was, for sure, a strange and unusual happening.

Sis, a Pop Machine, and Me

Sis was always up for a prank, and always happy to join us at Mischler's Lounge, an Irish pub a short walk from the dorm.

We all loved Mischler's, where we would go if we had some loose change for a beer (although Sis preferred Scotch), and then head back to the dorm to get into our PJ's and have peanut butter sandwiches and chocolate milk in the kitchen before bed check.

At other times, if any of us had an extra dime, it was off to the basement for a pop from the vending machine. The pop cooler was a slider-type of vending thing with multiple racks inside. The "Ideal 85T" model in the dorm basement was white with green lettering on the front ("Fresh up with 7Up!").

The machine opened by a cumbersome top lid; you chose your beverage, slid the glass bottle along a metal rack to the edge, put your dime in, and voila! The bottle was pulled free from its prison through a small gate at the top, and into thirsty hands.

One day I had a "great idea," and urged Sis to visit the pop machine with me, where "we can get all the pop we want, for free!"

"Let's go," said Sis, always eager for free. As we lifted the pop machine lid, I produced two straws and a can opener from my bathrobe pocket.

"Okay," I said to Sis in a whisper, "here's how we do it..."

With the bottles still securely held between the metal racks, I pried the lids off two bottles of Coke; handed Sis a straw and smiled.

"Just put your head into the pop machine, Sis," I said, "and have a free Coke!"

"Far out!" said Sis, putting a straw into her Coke bottle.

After sucking all the pop out of our bottles with the straws, we then recapped the bottles, feeling sorry for the poor thirsty customers that would pay their dime later and receive an empty Coke bottle for their troubles...but not sorry enough to not do it again the next week.

After that, though, Catholic guilt got the better of us and we decided that this trick would just have to be remembered for its creativity and not for its repetitiveness.

Sleeping Beauty

My friend Mary W. and I were seventeen years old when we started nursing school. It had been only a few months since we roamed the halls of our nun-infested high school, a girls-only place filled with young teens in stinky blue-serge uniforms. We had youth and immaturity on our side; otherwise we might have chosen some other career.

Mary was tall and slim with kind brown eyes, an Irish face, dimpled chin, and pug nose. She spoke quickly, like her Irish mother, and often had to repeat herself to be understood, her words tumbling over themselves in their haste to be the first ones out of her mouth.

Our rooms in the Mercy dorm were small, and sparsely furnished. The room consisted of a brown metal or wooden bed with a thin lumpy mattress, a scarred wooden desk, and a metal side chair that hurt your bottom if you sat too long.

There was a small closet near the door and a tiny porcelain sink for washing up in the morning. The "general bathroom" was down the hall, with sinks, showers, toilet stalls and a couple of huge cast iron tubs for long soaks.

What I liked best about Mary was her kindness and loyalty. You never heard Mary gossip, you never heard her complain about anyone, ever. Mary seemed more concerned about you then about herself. She had a way of turning the conversation back to you and she did it fast. Mary talked fast, she walked fast and she joked fast—she reminded me of an auctioneer. Sometimes I got dizzy.

At Marian Hall, Mary slept...a lot. I think she exhausted herself from all that rapid-fire talking. When classes and homework were done, Mary could be found in her bed, sleeping—a recovery process so deep, that she could not wake up in the morning.

Here is a typical morning routine:

It would begin with her Big Ben hand-wound alarm clock shrilling loudly, urging her awake, but failing in the task. Mary slept on. No one had as much success with waking Mary as I did, for I lived in the room across the hall and looked forward to the daily battle of getting Mary on her feet.

"Mary, hurry, wake up, you'll miss breakfast!"

Mary was not a breakfast eater, a fact that astonished me, as I relished a hospital cafeteria breakfast like a lung sought oxygen.

"I can't eat till I'm alive, and I'm not alive yet!" she muttered, "It's way too early."

"It's not early, kiddo, get up and get moving...I'm off to breakfast...don't you dare go back to sleep!

"It's Beaver today at 7:30, she's teaching isolation technique—can't wait to see her in that yellow gown...she'll be so totally Beaver!"

"Bed, miss bed..." I heard Mary murmur, sleep still in her voice, and turning around, I saw her stumbling after me down the long, dimly lit corridor past the phone booth, past the lounge to the shared dorm showers. Success again! Mary's on her feet!

Mary was and still is my trusted friend; one who could keep a friend's secrets, a trait that would stay with her all her life. Her sometimes-quiet ways belied a devilish sense of humor and a love for pranks and mischief, a devotion we shared. Mary, when awake, was a valued accomplice in the many "Mercy Girls" pranks that the class of 1963 would accomplish during three years of nursing school.

Going Around with Father

As student nurses in a Catholic hospital, we were required to take turns "going around with Father." This did not mean square dancing with the good priest. It meant we had to accompany Father Krupa, the Hospital Chaplain as he administered Holy Communion to bed-ridden Catholics on the wards. The student would meet Father at six-thirty a.m. for the communion rounds, and then rush to eat breakfast and be ready for clinicals or classes afterwards. It was the most annoying task!

It left little time for my usual hearty breakfast, so after a few rounds with Father, I decided to stop going. Avoidance coping.

Well, can you imagine the grief this decision visited upon me?

Once more, I received an invitation to Sister Mary Ethel's office where her stern, unhappy gaze heated my face up like a marshmallow over a campfire.

She did not accept my explanation that "going with Father" deprived me of much needed sleep and shortened my breakfast time. I think I stressed nutritional needs.

She was not amused. "You are campused, Miss Mumme, for the following two weeks. You need to think more about your responsibilities as a Catholic nursing student and less about breakfast."

My punishment was endured, but I never went around with Father again. I don't know who had to fill in for me, but I hope they enjoyed it far more than I ever did. And I apologize to them today for being such an inconsiderate ignoramus.

Chapter Four

Light at the End
of the Hospital Tunnel

(Senior Year)

Third Year Antics

Senior year was all about intensive hospital clinical experience. We worked long hours, all shifts and our nursing knowledge, skills and nursing intuition grew beyond our expectations (and perhaps the nuns, as well.)

And therefore...possibly...likely (surely?) we would pass our state exams and actually become Registered Nurses in New York State in 1963.

So we approached that final year with a blend of anxiety, curiosity, and hope. Would we make it?

But before the end of that final year of study, we had a few major clinical placements to get through. There was a three-month psychiatric nursing experience at a hospital near New York City, and a two-day local religious retreat where "silence at all times" was the golden rule to improve our Catholic souls. Let me tell you first, about the religious retreat.

The Religious Retreat Where I Did Not Retreat

Attending a religious retreat during our senior year was mandatory, and I guess the good sisters thought we needed the spiritual experience to deepen our nursing experience, but it actually was more like torture—for me at least. No music, no talking, no escaping.

For two days, we were trapped in a large Victorian mansion on Delaware Avenue near downtown Buffalo. Nuns ran it, this time dressed in black. We spent two long nights in this bleak stone and brick mausoleum with ivy creeping and strangling every window. We were prisoners who were told to pray.

Some of us prayed for our souls and the souls of others.

I am certain I did not. I was, instead, looking for diversion.

I recall a long curved staircase off a central hall, carpeted so deeply that your footsteps never made a sound (obviously part of the plan: no loud footsteps...might lead to dancing or running or something).

There were tall metal racks at the bottom of the staircase holding religious pamphlets. The racks needed dusting. Some of us actually read the holy leaflets.

I did not.

As you headed up the stairs to the second floor where our bedrooms were located, you couldn't miss seeing an imposing stained glass window, and, in front, a religious statue atop a tall wooden pedestal. That would be St. Jude, a heavy plaster statue about two feet high. He was holding a staff in his left hand and a round picture of Jesus in the other. St. Jude is best known as the patron saint for lost causes and desperate situations.

In the New Testament, St. Jude urged the faithful to persevere in any environment of harsh, difficult circumstances.

"Perfect," I muttered, "glad you're here," gazing intently at the statue, "the patron saint of desperate cases; the helper of the hopeless."

Well, I continued, "Here I am, and holy cow, am I desperate. I could use some help to get through these next two days. So please, St. Jude, help me hang loose in here and not get in trouble, but most of all, not get caught at any shenanigans I might think up."

A silent lunch, then orientation from the nuns in black (*they* could talk), then prayers before supper, then supper, then "quiet time" for more prayer and reflection on our mortal souls. Then bedtime and an early morning for mass and breakfast. I remember struggling with it all. I needed some action.

Later that night, I waited until everyone seemed settled in their rooms. I saw that my friend, Moe was in the shower.

"Perfect!" I thought.

Moe is the perfect victim; she responds well to torture.

I quietly made my way down to the staircase landing, made sure there were no nuns around and stole St. Jude off his perch.

"Come with me, dear."

He was heavier than I had thought. I put him in my pillowcase, climbed the stairs, and went down the hall to Moe's room.

"Here you go, Jude." (By now we were on a first-name basis.)

I whispered soft words of encouragement and placed him carefully in Moe's bed, under her pillow. Then I went to my own bed, smiling.

Moe told me later that when she crawled into bed after her shower, she sighed with sleepy exhaustion, put her head on her pillow and cracked her head on St. Jude.

She pulled him out and then screamed, "Mummeeeee!" St. Jude had bumped her head, but she knew who was responsible—and it was not St. Jude.

Now there was absolutely no talking at the Retreat House, and especially no screaming. Moe could have been in trouble for not keeping her vow of silence, but the nuns never heard her misery.

I can't recall today how St. Jude made it back to his perch on the staircase landing, but I do know that the eagle-eyed nuns never missed him. At least they never mentioned his absence to me. I think he enjoyed the trip around the mansion that night. I like to think his travels relieved his isolation a bit.

The next night I short-sheeted Moe's bed, and maybe a few others while I was at it. She laughs about her torture today, but back then I think she was not amused.

Mealtime was especially tortuous; we had to enter the dining room single file, and of course, silently, stand at our assigned table until Sister flipped a button on a recording, which then blasted out the mealtime prayer.

The machine sat on a small table at the front of the room near the door. The record repeated the same prayer, meal after meal: "Where God is-s-s-s-s, love is-s-s-s-s..."

Same prayer, same droning voice. Torture. Sister would wait for the prayer to stop, then, *click*, and the prayer would be over.

We could then sit down and eat; again, in absolute silence. Three times a day. Torture.

By suppertime that first day, I was thinking about pulling the plug on the machine. But as I watched the nun's finger flicking the button to begin and end our mealtime prayer, I began to wonder if I could, instead, ramp up the speed a little. Like the cadence of an auctioneer's voice, the prayer would then "sing" to us, giving the Mercy Girls some comic relief.

The next morning, enlisting Mary as lookout, (using sign language to indicate my intentions) we went to the dining room early.

Mary was always a willing accomplice and sometimes she could improve greatly on a planned prank. She was a great partner. Making certain that we were alone in the room, I flipped the switch, increasing the machine speed. We then beat a hasty, but well-advised retreat over to our assigned table to await the morning prayers. I had never in my life anticipated prayer quite so much as that morning in the dining room.

Minutes later, our classmates began to file in. Standing at our tables, Mary and I waited in fierce anticipation as the nun came in. She walked silently and solemnly to the player and pushed the button. *Gibberish, gibberish, gibberish...gibberish, gibberish, gibberish,* said the machine feverishly.

I was ecstatic. It was perfect! My classmates were tittering and Sister was apoplectic. Her face was pinched into a rage. She glared at us. That nun was ready to kick some serious butt and take down names.

"Who is responsible for this? This is outrageous! To have so little respect for these prayers! I tell you, again girls, that this is outrageous! I want the guilty party or parties to see me after breakfast in my office. This will not be tolerated! You have my word on that!"

Well, you can guess by now that my colleagues knew who was responsible, but would never say (we couldn't talk, of course, so how could they turn me in)? I could feel furtive eyes looking my way and then sliding away, lest they betray me. And they never did.

Nothing ever came of the sister's threat that day. No one ever came forward. And to our surprise, the retreat house never reported the incident. How we laughed about it later, when we could talk.

I loved that prank. It made the retreat bearable for me. I thanked St. Jude the next day, too, when I left the retreat house. I think I actually winked at him...and maybe he winked back.

The Nervous Disorder Hospital

Notice: Students Changed Forever by Psychiatric Clinical Experience! Not always for the better!

It was a stormy, fog-filled day when I arrived in New York City for my three-month psychiatric nursing training after an all-night train ride from Buffalo. A brief look at the glory of Grand Central Station, then I and some other Mercy Girls were herded onto a yellow bus to a nearby psychiatric facility in the suburbs outside New York City. Our mental health training was about to begin.

We drove down a long driveway to the student residence, a dark, looming, three storied building with dormer rooms in the eaves. I could see other buildings through the mist. As we were shown to our rooms by the Housemothers, I recall thinking that the place and everything in it was dark: somber, dull, poorly lit halls, with woodwork dark and grimy, in need of refinishing; dark metal beds in tiny warren-like student rooms; dark dressers the color of root beer.

The nursing instructor's offices were on the first floor along with the classrooms. After the cool grandeur of Grand Central Station, the nurses' dorm felt eerily dark as a cave and I was soon to feel like one of its cave bats.

Later that morning, I noticed one of the hospital buildings across the yard. The fog had lifted and I saw lots of glittering, multi-paned windows lit from inside, windows with a few solitary faces looking out. A shivery, shuddered place that waited for us—a group of neophyte, nervous student nurses not prepared for their future task of care.

Three months of confusion, fright and trepidation—that sums up our psychiatric rotation. Exposure to the world of the mentally ill was a shock for most of us—that we survived it and still found time for a few pranks and some fun was a mystery— or was it a miracle, or perhaps a necessity?

After orientation the next day, we were scheduled for our various clinical assignments, as well as classroom instruction. We learned about mental illness and disorders, the most modern treatments and medicines of the 60s, as well as all aspects of psychiatric nursing.

I remember a day shift assignment, shortly after I had arrived, on the "Chronic" ward. The "Chronic" ward held long term, chronically ill patients. Some had been "chronic" for years there. The hospital ward doors were always locked to prevent escape and students and staff carried large sets of keys that jangled loudly when we walked, announcing our presence.

Passing out the noontime medicines on the ward that day, I passed an elderly woman sitting in the hall. She was strapped to her chair with white cloth restraints, making jerking movements, in a vain attempt to become free.

Suddenly she lurched her body and the chair forward into me, yelling, "You little slimy crapper! Three bitches to you and Frank! Fuck you and all the fucks in this town!"

Shocked to hear such words coming from an old woman, I think I murmured, "Yes, dear, I understand..." and continued down the hall.

I could hear her calling after me, "Fuck you still!" snarling obscenities and taking the lord's name in vain in the most original way.

To prevent further injury, I quickly learned to do a rapid side step when passing by her, while wishing her a cheerful, "Good morning!"

Another patient would grab my arm as I walked by, steer me to the window and point to a statue of a saint in the garden.

"I really must go now, you can see that my father is out there waiting for me."

How to reply to this sad, earnest request? I never knew whether to go along, make excuses or just walk away. Training had not prepared me for the right answer.

Usually, I muttered something like, "Hmm, I see," until I became a little more experienced and could distract her with a glass of orange juice or the TV in the patient lounge.

A few minutes later, she would be back at the window again, with another student nurse, asking to be let out to see her father in the garden. Resignation mixed with hope hung over these patients like a cloak around their shoulders.

Treatments for some of these patients suffering from depression or schizophrenia consisted of electroshock therapy and/or insulin coma therapy. These psychiatric treatments induced seizures and were thought to improve illness outcomes, (i.e. behavior) but assisting at any of these procedures was painful for us, as our patients seemed to suffer so much. We dreaded taking patients for these sessions as much as they did.

Miss Godek Diagnoses Me

One day, soon after our arrival, I met Miss Godek, the Superintendent of Student Nurses. A nurse as odd as a Freud disciple, she had called me to a "meeting" to "discuss an issue with me" after two weeks of classes.

"There's something you're not telling me," Miss Godek said, while staring sternly into my face.

Miss Godek's office was a small room close to the front door of the nurse's residence. That way she could watch the comings and goings of her charges from here, and call them in for an "issue meeting" as the need arose.

A large woman with unnaturally small grey eyes, Miss Godek had an odd way of creating a mental health monster out of any simple occurrence. I thought she was as loony as the Mad Hatter, only with a nurse's cap perched on her head.

"Not telling you, Miss Godek?" I murmured, as I stared at the surface of the old wooden desk in the instructor's office.

The words, "I love Charlie" had been carved into the top of the scarred desk and I had been wondering who Charlie was and then wondered who had loved him.

Miss Godek leaned forward, interrupting my thoughts, and hissed: "You neglected to bring your books to my class today. We need to discuss your rationale."

I was flummoxed. What did she mean? Rationale for what? Yes, I had forgotten my textbook for her weekly Nursing Care of the Mentally Ill Patient, in my haste to be on time for her class.

I felt confused, "My rationale?"

Her eyes wandered to the carved inscription...*Had she carved it herself*, I wondered.

Miss Godek gave me a small smile and said, her tiny eyes narrowing, "You forgot your books on purpose, did you not, Miss Mumme? I do think that, from what I have observed of you since your arrival last week, that I see an atypical behavior pattern here...maladaptive perhaps...such thoughtlessness will not serve you well in your future months here at this facility. Perhaps there are unconscious coping mechanisms at work...anxiety issues...what are your thoughts on the matter, Miss Mumme?"

"Huh?" I said articulately.

Okay, so my response was maybe a bit inadequate, but it was the best I could do at the time. I thought longingly of Sister Mary Ethel, at least she always made sense to me.

"I am seeing some maladaptive behaviors here, oh, yes I am indeed, Miss Mumme. And you need to know that these types of behaviors can inhibit a student's ability to adjust to particular situations, such as this placement, and will prevent you from adapting to future demands of life."

I said nothing.

She went on, "I see, also, that you can be non-communicative."

"Well..." I began, thinking fast. But I could think of nothing.

"I think it goes without saying, Miss Mumme, that we will talk again soon, oh, yes, I think we will. That's all for now, you may return to your room."

I left her office, convinced that I had met my first insane nurse. I went to my room, got Yolanda and we went for a Coke with plenty to talk about.

Yolanda Sleeps in the Bathtub

In the student nurses dorm, there was one bathroom between each of two rooms. It had a large claw foot bathtub, good for long soaks, for which we never had time.

Yolanda and I shared a small, narrow bedroom, and this proved to be difficult. For I was a solitary pop drinker who left my empties all over the place...on desks, on the floor...and under the beds...a room not made for excess empties? This annoyed Yolanda. It did not annoy me. "Trouble in River City" was ahead of us, for I did not know back then how obstinate I could sometimes be.

I'm hardly in our door one day, when Yolanda starts yelling:

"I can't stand it anymore! You and your empties! There are more pop bottles around here than Carter has little liver pills! And you never take them back to the bottle room! Never! It smells like a Coca-Cola factory! I can't stand it!"

I looked around the room, and then looked at Yo, mesmerized by her iguana green hair, perfectly coiffed in a pageboy style. I had generously offered to dye her hair the day before, so that she could be a "silver-haired blonde." Well, THAT did not work out in her favor! Her hair was an odd, pea shade of green, with copper highlights.

Yo had a lot to be angry about. Yo had more than one thing to be angry about. She announced that, from here on in, she was sleeping in the bathtub. And good riddance to me!

With that, she grabbed her blankets and pillow and left me, choosing to sleep in the claw foot bathtub. I was astonished, and then felt guilty. I was nineteen years old and an insensitive clod.

I took all the empty pop bottles back to the basement bottle room. I said I was sorry to Yo, and it must have been enough, because the next day she came back and slept in her own bed.

Yolanda and I still laugh about this story today, and I still apologize for frustrating her to the point where she chose a bathtub for a bed.

Brother Arthur, Tall and Tortured

He was six feet, eight inches tall, and had to duck when he went through doorways. A nursing student from New York City, and a Christian Brother, Brother Arthur was doing his psychiatric nursing rotation at the same time as our group from Buffalo. I am not sure he thought this was good timing on his part, but we became friends and enjoyed practical jokes at each other's expense.

Brother Arthur had a small room near the dorm's front door, almost directly across from Miss Godek's office. This location makes practical jokes all the more dangerous and exciting.

Getting caught by Miss Godek would mean lectures, psychoanalytical diagnoses, and possible dismissal.

The pranks began small and soon became more daring.

One night when Brother Arthur was on the three to eleven shift, I snuck into his room with a canister vacuum, plugged it into the outlet attached to the ceiling light bulb, made sure the light was off, then flipped the vacuum switch to "ON."

He had quite a noisy surprise when he returned to his room, turned his light on and heard the sudden high-pitched scream of the vacuum cleaner. He told me later that he was so startled that he jumped high onto his bed, hitting his head on the ceiling, cursing and fumbling madly for the chain to silence the beastly machine before anyone came to investigate.

Later, I convinced Kathy M., a prank-willing Mercy Girl, that our next escapade would be harmless and we would never be caught. Kathy looked doubtful, but was my willing accomplice.

The following night we snuck into Brother Arthur's room. He was working the night shift, so the coast was clear. We struggled a bit, but got the mattress from his bed and spirited it out the door and down the hall. We hid it under Louise S.'s bed and she was surprised, but willing. We were sweating with glee and delighted at our success.

The next morning we had to return the bedding to its rightful owner before our clinicals began. Our only problem was that we had not anticipated Miss Godek being in her office early. Now we had trouble. If we were seen carrying a mattress down the hall, we would have had a hard time explaining it. Oh, that Godek, she would have really enjoyed finding us out. We imagined her saying,

"Come here, you two, so that I can hang some mental disorder on you."

We got that mattress back somehow without old "Beady Eyes" seeing us. Sometimes God smiles on hapless student nurses...or at least He did that morning.

Brother Arthur never did top that deed. I recall him saying that the Mercy Girls were the best pranksters ever, and the brightest bunch of nurses he'd ever met.

We left our placement three months later and went home gratefully to Mercy and Marian Hall. We left mentally ill patients to continue struggling against their demons and monsters. I'm not sure we make any difference in their difficult lives.

Our psych clinical was a really difficult rotation, but the fun we created for ourselves helped make it bearable. Whether it was walks with Louise, or hitching rides to Rye Town beach with the other "Maureens," I think we all used humor and off-duty outings to survive amidst the chaos.

Marking the Enemy's Position

I was glad to be back at Mercy Hospital and to nuns that, at least made some sense when they spoke. Suspicious, but rational, that's how the Mercy nuns appeared to me.

We were finishing our final year of training, and that year our rooms were on the third floor. One Monday night after study hour, I was in the lounge, having chocolate milk and staring at Sister Cyrilla's door across the hall. Sister lived on the same floor as we did and we all thought she was a spy, but if she was, we had no proof.

Deep in thought, I did not notice Mary come in until I heard her say, "Mumme, what are you plotting?"

"Oh, just marking the enemy's position."

"Sister Cyrilla?" (Mary always knew my mind's working.) "What for?" Mary sat down, always interested in what might become a prank.

"Mary, I need to figure out how long Sister is away at chapel tonight. I think I would need about an hour...or maybe an hour and fifteen...just to be on the safe side."

"Safe side of what? What are the plans and plots, Mumme?"

"Well, if all goes according to Hoyle, I think we can empty her room of furniture, store it in the lounge, and then move it all back before she gets back from chapel. We'll need a lookout to head her off at the pass if she shows up early. Now there's a prank we can be proud of! Best one ever!"

"Gees, Mumme, I think that's too iffy...even for us...maybe we can just do Moe's room when she's in the shower..."

Mary looked doubtful, which was unusual. Mary usually was a willing cohort on most of our capers, so this gave me pause.

"Hmmm," I muttered, "it's such a great idea, but maybe you're right, maybe it is too risky. So, okay, we just empty Moe's room." Poor Moe, always such a perfect victim; her reactions to tricks continued to be superb!

"Anyway, we have to be all done before lights out."

We gathered some Mercy Girls to serve as furniture movers, then watched and waited until Moe went for her nightly shower. In a matter of minutes, her room was cleared out, right down to her books. We hid it all in Sara S.'s room, who said she was now a bit crowded, but did not complain.

Moe came back to her room, freshly showered with a towel tightly wrapped around her head. We all watched from across the hall, waiting in great anticipation as she walked into her room.

Soon we heard a scream. Ah, that Moe could scream like a woman having a mammogram.

Running into the lounge, Moe saw me and yelled, "Mumme, you damn hellion, where's my bed? Hell, where's my stuff? God, you are all so nuts!"

We all surrounded her, having a good laugh. Then she reminded us that bed check was in five minutes and it would be really good if she had a bed to be in when the Housemothers did bed check. I don't know how, but we got all her furniture back in her room before the Housemother came by with her flashlight. Perfect prank.

The Great Galoshes Caper

Perhaps one of our greatest acts of buffoonery in senior year was the "great galoshes caper." This gag was played on a group of visiting nuns from a nearby convent. They came to our dorm for an evening meeting in the auditorium, then usually had refreshments and mingled with the other Mercy sisters.

It was a cold and snowy night that winter of 1962, and the wind was howling, and pushing at windows, trying to get in.

Mary and I were standing at the third floor staircase landing, peering down to the first floor, and looking for Madge U. We were waiting for her to come back from a food raid in the dorm's kitchen.

Madge was an expert at finding goodies in the nun's kitchen. She would crawl through the "pass-through" window between the kitchen and auditorium, take some desserts off the trays, and then rearrange the goodies so nothing looked suspicious. This, she had down to a science: run to kitchen-open corrugated metal "pass-through"; get desserts; shove into her bag; crawl through the "pass-through"; take treasures to hungry students in the lounge. Madge had organizational skills that would be essential to a nursing career.

Mary and I wore bathrobes and slippers (the evening outfit of choice after a day of hospital rounds), watching below as about twenty nuns from the nearby Catholic high school began arriving for their meeting.

Shaking the snow from their coats, the sisters removed their black rubber boots (galoshes, as they were called in the early 60s, the kind that fit over shoes, and close snugly with a satisfying *click* when the metal buckles snap shut).

They put their overshoes neatly in pairs on the stair steps, up one side and down the other, leaving a path clear in the middle for walking the stairs.

As the nuns went into the auditorium, Mary and I stared down at the identical galoshes lining both sides of the stairs, our prankster-brains in overload.

We looked at each other, "At least forty pairs of boots—are you thinking what I'm thinking?"

We nodded silently to each other, and then ran down the stairs. We quickly but quietly mixed up all the boots. We put a large sized boot with a small; a size 9 was paired with a size 6, and so on. We made sure the boots were left as neatly as before. As the boots were identical, there was no apparent disturbance to the arrangement. We saw a neat black sea of rubber mayhem—little mismatched boots lining the smooth worn steps of Marian Hall.

We ran back up to the third floor landing, watching and waiting. Soon, the nuns finished their meeting, and came to the stairs for their boots.

"Why, Sister Mary Assumption, my boots don't seem to fit me now!" exclaimed one of the nuns, probably wondering whether she had gained weight by eating two pieces of cake that night.

"I don't understand it," another muttered aloud to no one in particular, "one boot fits, but the left one is way too small!"

We heard one of the sisters say, "I can't believe it, what in heaven's name is the matter with my galoshes, they're all so wrong!"

Mary and I hugged each other in absolute glee and delight at the sight below. It took everything we had to keep from laughing out loud. We covered our mouths to prevent any loud guffaws from escaping. It was the best prank ever. We thought we should receive the Prank Pulitzer Prize, for God's sake!

It took the poor sisters over an hour to sort out their boots and find their properly sized galoshes. They were in a frenzied state of befuddlement, but eventually they sorted it all out.

Why this trick was never reported to Sister Mary Ethel, I will never know. I can't imagine the visiting nuns would not have been a little suspicious over the mixed up galoshes. But as luck would have it, we never got into any trouble over our "great galoshes caper." Luck of the Irish.

Chapter Five
Working for Pennies

One Last Beer at Mischler's

It was almost over. We had survived nursing school and were nearing graduation. Evening was settling in and I was having one last beer with Mary at Mischler's.

Moe came in to join us, and with a toss of her page boy bob, threw our newly created Mercy yearbook (*MAGNIFICAT, 1963*) on the table.

"It's a great yearbook, wait til you see the photos!"

Then she pointed to page six, the FOREWORD, saying, "Why didn't someone tell me that I was now a mature professional woman—why am I always the last one to know? I think I need a beer, quick."

Mary and I read the following:

Within these pages we have attempted to re-enter the many thresholds through which we have passed in our efforts to become ideal Catholic nurses. Through knowledge, many doors have been opened, exposing us to rewarding, promising experiences from which developed the pattern we followed in becoming mature, professional women. "MAGNIFICAT 1963" is our effort to recapture these formative years at Mercy Hospital School of Nursing, that we may be able to pause once again in reviewing the phases which were responsible for attaining our goal.

Agreeing, I muttered, "Well, we've had experiences, all right. But the only door I enjoyed opening was the exit!"

Thumbing through the pages, I wondered about the reality of those three years not reflected in that book: the hard work, late nights, raw exposure to the mentally and physically ill; the rules and regulations, the lack of ability to raise our voice and to be heard? It could/would not be told, nor reflected in the pages of our yearbook.

"Yup," said Mary, "we had doors open to us, that's a fact! And out we go! Let's have a toast! Here's to three years of bondage, but also to three years of dear friendships that made it all bearable!"

I smiled, sipping my ten-cent draft beer, remembering. The time and the place had molded me. I knew, looking back, that three years of nursing school had been so very difficult, but yet, somehow, someway, most of us had actually become graduate nurses. Interpreting and assimilating the process had been difficult for me back then. I would need years of reflection and years of nursing practice to be able to put the parts into a whole. But I also knew, even then, that the goal of becoming a "mature professional woman" remained an elusive one that might take a few years of work for me.

But, to my mind, agreeing with Mary, the best experience of all had been the dear friendships we had made at Mercy, a common bond that held us and supported us like a safety net, despite long hours of ward duty, the challenges thrown our way by nuns, instructors, physicians, and patients. The joy and satisfaction of that bond would stay with us all our lives, enhancing and enriching our world. Beyond the student work at Mercy, we had made friends that would last a lifetime. And for that, I am forever grateful.

My Driving Displeases Doctors

I graduated from Mercy Hospital School of Nursing in the summer of 1963. I went on to patch myself together with bits of nursing knowledge into a young twenty-year-old Registered Nurse with a full-time pediatric nursing position at Kenmore Mercy Hospital in the suburbs of Buffalo. Both Mary and Gerrie P. worked there as well.

Our starting salary was $2.25 an hour, and we worked an eight-hour shift, either days or afternoons. We worked most weekends; I think we got one weekend off a month, and worked most holidays as well.

The work was satisfying, hard and the little kids sweet but sick, sick, sick. Treatments included medicines, oxygen tanks, and ice baths for fevers. I always hated the ice baths, when we had to put a small child in ice-cold sheets and ice cubes to reduce a high fever. I recall the screaming anguish and then, soon after, the deep sleep that would be induced by the cold. I don't think they use that treatment anymore to lower a baby's temperature.

It always made me feel guilty to cause such anguish to a child, but I carried out doctor's orders faithfully. WE DID NOT QUESTION DOCTOR'S ORDERS in those early years of practice. (That would come later, with more confidence and nursing knowledge and a keen sense of the patient's condition.)

We would eventually become the patient WATCHERS. We could tell when something was not right and we learned to "keep an eye." We used intuition and found it to be an important tool in our practice of nursing.

There was more autonomy as a staff nurse than we had had during nursing school, but we were still controlled by the doctors, charge nurses, and hospital supervisors. In looking back, I think it must have annoyed me, because sometimes my prank self resurfaced, with some unfortunate results.

One day, at Kenmore Mercy, I was a few minutes late for work, and rushed my 1960 Ford Falcon (with "Ford-O-Matic" drive) into the hospital parking lot. Frustrated that I could not find a parking space anywhere, I suddenly noticed the Chief of Staff's reserved parking spot...empty! Well, I was late, after all, and maybe this was his day off? So without hesitation, I pulled into his space and beat a hasty retreat to my ward.

It wasn't twenty minutes later when the hospital loudspeaker boomed the error of my ways to all listening and urged the guilty party to "Remove your car at once or have it towed!" How could I think I could ever get away with that?

The Chief was waiting for me in the parking lot beside my little car, a look of disbelief and anger on his face. His cheeks were red and his lips an odd purple color. He was sputtering mad.

With my keys jangling in my hand, I muttered, "Gee, is that your parking spot? What must I have been thinking?" and drove off to park in a less-privileged area.

Nothing came of this misdeed, but Mary said later that she knew it was my evil doings when the loudspeaker sounded off. Mary sometimes knew me better than I knew myself.

Later that snowy winter, I had another parking lot crisis at Kenmore Mercy. I had just finished my day shift, when I got the Falcon caught in a snowdrift near the back door of the hospital. A good-hearted physician, driving by, saw my dilemma and pushed me out with his car. He should have thought better of the idea.

I thanked him profusely, as he got back into his car ahead of me. I got in my car, gave it some gas (well, maybe a bit too much gas) to ensure I cleared the edge of the snow bank and plowed into the doctor's rear bumper.

Smash, crunch! I heard, and watched in horror as his car suddenly jolted forward, his neck snapping backward. Gosh, when he emerged from that car he was as angry as the chief of staff, but this time I was innocent of any prank, my only guilt consisted of bad driving in a hospital parking lot.

I think those two doctors warned their colleagues to steer clear of any young nurse attempting to drive a cream-colored Falcon anywhere near their vicinity, because I never had any more trouble in the parking lot.

Angry Nun Seeks My Head on a Platter

The head nurse at Kenmore Mercy approached me one Monday morning to say I was wanted on the phone. Finishing diapering a little one, I covered him and put up the crib side rail before leaving the room. I could hear the baby wailing, "Come back!" as I went down the hall to the nurse's station.

I picked up the phone and was shocked to hear Sister Mary Ethel's voice. It had been only four months since graduation, and I had forgotten the feeling of dread that voice could have on me…like fingernails screeching down a blackboard.

"Miss Mumme, this is Sister Mary Ethel."

I could feel fear grab my heart, as I suddenly felt her old control and domination.

"Morning, Sister, how are you?" I was acting calm and cheery, but it was a lie I told myself.

Ignoring my attempt at politeness, Sister said, "Miss Mumme, I need to see you to discuss a matter of great urgency."

I could still hear my little patient howling his disappointment at my leaving him.

Distractedly, I responded, "Great urgency, Sister?"

"Yes, some thing's come up and I need to see you in my office here at Mercy as soon as possible."

Her request did not surprise me, but my fear remained. I needed to be brave and resolute. For you see, I was lucky enough to have been forewarned of Sister's impending telephone call; "tipped off" by one of the Mercy Girls, who had connections. I had been told that Sister Mary Ethel was "gunning for Mumme with a holy vengeance."

Here's what happened…One of my last pranks in school had come unraveled…right into the large, angry lap of the Big E. During our last week of school, our spirits ran high and I had penned a "letter" poking fun at Sister Mary Ethel. Not only did the letter make very unflattering comments about her, I had added insult to injury by pretending the author was Sister Cyrilla.

How we all had laughed at the letter "signed" by Sister Cyrilla as I showed it to a few classmates in the student lounge that day. Then putting the letter in my notebook, I carelessly left the notebook with damning document in the lounge, to be found later by the authorities. Classic Mumme.

Now she was seeking my head on a platter. Her voice on the phone made me think of icicles hanging from frozen rooftops, ready to fall and puncture someone (me).

Well, there was only one way out of this, so I said, "Oh, Sister, I can't possibly meet you. I am much too busy with my new job. You can't imagine how I love my new job. I'm working on the Pediatrics Unit and...."

Sister interrupted me, her voice dripping anger, "Well, when can you meet with me, Miss Mumme? Next week? I can make some time for you next week."

But I had prepared my excuse beforehand, just in case.

"Why, never, Sister," I said, "I can never meet with you because my life is much too busy."

Well, yes, it was a lame excuse, but what was I to do? I could not return to Mercy and endure her wrath. The letter had been small-minded and mean of me, and I regret writing it today. But back then? I cannot recall a single kernel of remorse. Shame, yes; remorse, no.

The conversation went on for a while longer, she insisting and me dodging, but I knew that any meeting would be sheer disaster for me.

Then, suddenly, I heard a sharp *bong* in my ear. Sister had hung up on me*! Sorry*, I whispered, as I gently replaced the handset onto the phone cradle gently.

I turned and walked down the hall to check on my tiny patient in Room 305, looking forward and not back. It was twenty-five years before I returned to Mercy Hospital, years that ensured that the coast was clear, and that I would not have to endure the wrecking ball of Sister Mary Ethel's anger.

Hey! I Like School!

Despite all the school pranks and lunacy during the Mercy years, I did graduate, and eventually returned to school for a

Bachelor of Science in Nursing in 1988, and a Master's of Science in Nursing in 1994.

My master's thesis involved research into the history of nursing friendships and the importance of friendship and caring for both nurses and the nursing profession. The research also uncovered (at least for me) some renegades in the early history of the nursing profession.

In articles I wrote for the now-defunct *Revolution–The Journal of Nurse Empowerment*, I commented that I had been a nursing school renegade, who managed to slip through the cracks of the "catch and expel all renegades system" so common in those years. "Nursing needs more renegades," I wrote, "...more original thinkers, independent spirits, and a few dreamers thrown in for good measure."

I suggested that nursing students search nursing history for examples of strong nursing leadership:

"Lavinia Dock, one of nursing's early leaders and the ultimate risk-taker, was a creative force who helped develop a still-uncharted profession. Dock had a voice of her own and risk-taking behaviors that saw her jailed on three occasions for her suffragist actions."

I had an affinity for strong-willed nurses, believing it was vital for our professional growth through time.

After forty-three years in nursing (eighteen of them in public health nursing in Canada), I retired from a much-loved profession. I look back on those years with gratitude and to my schooling with special fondness.

Gerrie, one of the "B-Group" Mercy Girls, had once commented that I was "an eccentric" in nursing school. I remember thinking, "Oh!" at the time, and being surprised.

Years later, Jake, my young grandson, was reading a book, and asked me the meaning of the word, "eccentric."

"Well," I replied, "eccentric means someone who is a little bit different from others, a non-conformist, a person who is maybe 'a bit of a maverick.' Sort of a free spirit."

I laughed and continued, "Why, do you know, Jake, that in my nursing school days, some of my classmates thought that I was eccentric?"

"Well, Grandma, excuse me, but you *are*, no offence!" he said.

So, there you have it, from the mouths of babes. The truth will set you free (or, at least make you smile).

In doing research for this memoir, I came across my student nursing record, signed and dated by Sister Mary Ethel on June 6, 1963. What must Sister have been thinking back then? Did she hesitate as she signed her name, officially endorsing my graduation and my future?

Did she think, *Maybe, just maybe, Miss Mumme might turn out all right?*

Well it's a long shot, she might have pondered, *she could go either way...time will tell with that one, that's for sure...*

Section 3

Maureen O'Connor Weber

Dreams die hard. My dream was to go to New York City and attend acting school. I would have given Sally Field serious competition. I could have been a better "Flying Nun" in the television series. After all, I had first-hand experience of being tormented by nuns from first grade to age twenty-one. Then again, I wouldn't have married a great guy whose name was Joe Weber and had three beautiful children and six beautiful grandchildren.

Ten years after graduating from Mercy Hospital School of Nursing, I read a newspaper article about two leading nursing organizations that advised all nurses have a four-year Baccalaureate of Science degree in Nursing. President Carter funded universities for this purpose. Niagara University had such a program. Three and a half years later, I became a "recycled" RN with a BS degree. Soon after, an opportunity to work for the local health department presented itself. I had worked in a local hospital and for a group of doctors as an office nurse, but found my true calling as a community health nurse. I found it to be the most autonomous role for a nurse. Besides knocking on someone's door to offer care, one had to be a good driver in all kinds of weather and to have a healthy respect for all kinds of animals that bite.

I continued working in public health for the reminder of my career. I retired after a long career that would not have been possible without the training I received at Mercy and the support I have had from the "Mercy Girls."

Chapter One
Freshman Year:
The New Recruit

Three Dollars a Day

On September 6, 1960, my mother and I signed a contract with a three-year Catholic diploma school of nursing in Buffalo, New York, called Mercy Hospital School of Nursing. Visions of my true calling of attending acting school in New York City were dashed to bits by reality. I had no money to pay for this dream. Little did I know how much my acting skills would come in handy during nursing training and as a Registered Nurse.

We had found our way to Marian Hall, the dorm building, where we sat across the desk from a very large nun who was the director of the nursing school. Instead of the usual black habit with white facing, she was in snow-white regalia. Sister Mary Ethel sat there looking like the Pillsbury Dough Boy.

"Why do you want to be a nurse?" she asked.

"I think that it's a good career for a woman," I replied, hoping to please her.

"If you think that you'll be making a lot of money as a nurse, you're mistaken. It is a calling from God to give loving care to everyone who is suffering."

Sister explained that the nursing school had a very structured program. First-year students attended Canisius College, an all-male school in Buffalo. After completing the first year at Canisius, the remaining two years consisted of classes in the dormitory building and other affiliated health institutions. The thirty-three month nursing program would provide a nursing diploma. Sister pointed out that The New York State Board of Education then required a licensing examination for registered nurses, saying, "I expect all my students to pass!"

With no further ado, Sister slid the contract across her desk for my mother and I to read. My mother's eyes zeroed in on "the School agrees to provide the student room and board directly through other institutions as foresaid at the rate of Three Dollars [$3.00] per day." My mother was a frugal person by nature and she knew a bargain when she saw one. Of course, the first year of college tuition would be costly, but not too bad. The three of us signed the contract and the deed was done.

Sister presented me with the *Student Handbook*. It was a tiny thirty-two-page blue book, but filled cover-to-cover with rules and regulations. With dread, I realized that this educational experience would be an extension of the previous twelve years of parochial rules and regulations.

My mother was always looking for ways to save money. "By the way," she said, "is there anyone else from the Niagara Falls area enrolled in the school? We could car pool."

Sister gave my mother the name of another young student, whose name was Emilie N. and little did I know then that we would become lifelong friends. Our fellow classmates and nursing instructors often mistook us for one another. Emilie had been educated in the public school system all of her life and was enthralled with the nuns. She thought that they were all wonderful despite our warnings. Throughout the three years, fellow students, myself included, educated her in ways to outfox the nuns.

The Admission Physical

It was "Admission Physical Day" at the school. I picked up Emilie at her home and we drove to Marian Hall. We were to report to Sister Mary Claver, who was in charge of student health services. We arrived in plenty of time and went to the exam room. There was another girl, Rachel W., waiting for her physical as well. She was friendly and very happy to be accepted at the school. Suddenly, a very tall nun dressed in white, swept into the room, barely keeping her balance. Her prominent front teeth made her speech sound funny. She resembled a great white bird of prey in flight with buckteeth.

"My name is Sister Mary Claver and I'll be asking you questions about your health. Afterwards, I'll be taking some blood from you. Any questions? Who wants to go first?"

Rachel volunteered to be the sacrificial lamb. Before I knew it, it was my turn. Sister wrapped a rubber strap around my upper arm, applied rubbing alcohol to the inside of my arm and attempted to insert a large needle into the vein. She kept missing but kept jabbing away anyway. I promptly fainted. The next thing I knew, I was in a hospital bed. My new friend from the Falls was in the bed next to me. She had fainted also. Smelling salts permeated the air.

"You'll be fine dear," said the big white nun. "I hope that nursing is a true calling for you and your friend."

Little did I know that I'd had my first encounter with the infamous Sister Bucky Beaver. No wonder I fainted.

Mommies Dearest

God bless the Housemothers! They were the guardians of the entire dormitory full of hormonal females. They were on duty 24/7 to protect and serve all, whether student or nun. Anyone who arrived at the front door pressed the doorbell and was interrogated about the nature of their visit. Upon Housemother Approval, entrance was granted. Surrounded in glass, the Housemother sat in the cockpit space and was able to survey the foyer. She would page the student to inform her that she had a visitor.

Curfew rules varied. Weekday curfew was 10:30 p.m., with lights out at 11:00 p.m. Extra privileges were granted to the senior students, depending on their time schedule. Special privileges had to be requested from the School of Nursing Office. It was a very controlled environment, almost like the students were being treated like they were novitiates. After all, Marian Hall was across the street from the nun's residence.

The first place students went to after class was to the Housemothers' glass enclosed cockpit, where everyone had their own mailbox. Happy faces meant the student had mail and sad faces meant no mail that day.

A total of eight Housemothers shared the awesome responsibility of guarding us. The Mothers who worked the day shift were familiar to all, while the Mothers working the night shift were not as well-known except at exam time. During this time, students would try and fool them by studying late into the night instead of sleeping in their beds. The majority of the Mothers were nice and fairly motherly with only one sour puss. The ultimate Housemother from Hell was in the future. She reigned at the psychiatric treatment center dormitory in Westchester County.

When we returned from Mischler's, the local watering hole, our beer breath would be overlooked. This bar was our favorite place to socialize. Patricia G. liked sitting in the booth, pressing a bell on the wall, so our waitress would appear to take our beer order.

The biggest responsibility of the Mother was to report to the Director when a young man came to pick up his date. There must have been a secret buzzer that rang in Sister Mary Ethel's (alias: The Big E) office when he appeared. He would be directed to sit in the waiting room area. The Big E would arrive and the interrogation would begin in earnest. Did he attend college or did he work full time somewhere? What religion did he practice? How long had he been seeing this certain young lady and what were his future plans? If Sister liked the young man, she made it a point to call the student into her office and ask her if she enjoyed her date the night before. Sister was full of advice for boyfriends and other worldly issues. She advised one student to end her friendship with a student whom she thought was a bad influence.

While cramming for final exams, we often would shove towels across the bottom of the doorframe to hide the light shining on our books. We drank massive cups of instant coffee to stay awake. Emilie drank so much coffee that she refuses to drink it to this day.

After study period, the noise level in the dorm was at high pitch. Junior and Senior students trying to sleep or getting ready for hospital duty would call the Mother for help in quieting unruly freshmen. She announced in a loud voice, "Keep the noise down...people are sleeping!" Her loud announcement actually woke sleeping students.

The Housemothers had awesome responsibilities. They made sure we were studying at our desks, were sleeping soundly in our beds, dating the right young man. WOW! I prefer nursing as a career!

Dorm Life

Marian Hall was an imposing four-story structure with a basement and a tunnel that connected the dormitory to the hospital. It housed approximately one hundred students who came from all over New York State and from other states as well.

I considered myself lucky to have a room to myself in the newer section of the dorm. The view from my window was that of another building with a brush of visible green grass. The room had a comfortable single bed, a dresser with a lamp, a desk and chair, a small sink and a roomy closet. Having shared a bedroom with an older sister all of my life, a room to myself was heaven.

The lounge in the older section of the dorm was where most of the students gathered to socialize, play cards, watch television, eat tuna fish sandwiches and smoke cigarettes. The male species was dissected for sexiness and cuteness, funny incidents were discussed and new, fun dance steps like the Twist were practiced. Help with plucking eyebrows, dying hair and borrowing clothes from one another was the norm. Dueling radios played from the individual rooms. One could hear "You Talk Too Much," "Cathy's Clown," "Walk Don't Run," and "The Twist," as you walked down the hallways.

Strict study hours ran from five p.m. to eight p.m. Everyone had to keep the door to their room open. This allowed the Housemother to see into the room and made sure that we were sitting at our desks, studying. If we were caught sleeping or lying on our beds or had a radio playing, Sister Mary Ethel would call us into her office for a very serious reprimand. No smoking was allowed in the rooms.

Once eight p.m. arrived, all hell broke loose. The public pay telephone would add to the noise level by ringing on the dot of eight. Carol M.'s boyfriend called her every night at eight exactly. She was known as a "goody two shoes" because she did all of her assignments on time, was immaculate in her personal and professional life, got top grades, and everyone liked her.

It didn't take long for Emilie and me to meet our fellow classmates. "Are you the girls from Niagara Falls?" was the reoccurring question. It sounded like we were from some foreign country instead of a city about thirty miles away from Buffalo. A lot of the students had gone to high school together and most were girls from South Buffalo. There were a fair number of students from out of town. These poor souls had to stay in the dorm month after month.

Of course, the students who were confined to the dorm for disciplinary reasons would entertain them. One student in particular, always seemed to be in trouble with Sister Mary Ethel. Her name was Maureen Mumme, a Kenmore girl who lived in the dorm. Because there were five Maureens in the class with Irish last names who had nicknames of Moe, these five were called by their last names. Mumme had a knack for inventing names for the nuns and had a unique way of pulling pranks.

The nuns were all given nicknames that seemed to match their personalities. Sister Mary Ethel became known as The Big E, Sister Mary Claver became Sister Bucky Beaver because of her buckteeth and Sister Mary Jean Baptist became Sister Lippes Loop. This nun was the Labor and Delivery nurse and instructor who reportedly had a shoe box filled with a contraceptive device known as the Lippes Loop that was inserted into the cervix to prevent pregnancy. Sister kept the devices that had been removed before a baby was delivered to prove that they didn't work. She would gleefully shake the box with great vigor and cackle like a witch.

Mumme seemed to be in detention frequently and made to stay in the dormitory over the weekend as punishment. This didn't deter her one bit as she found other ways to amuse herself by tormenting the Housemothers. She would call the Housemother from one of the public telephones and speak with a fake foreign accent. She would ask for a specific student with a garbled accent that the Housemother couldn't understand. Several minutes would go by with the Housemother thoroughly confused. Mumme would then simply hang up. Other times, she would call a Canisius College dorm and ask for a specific basketball player. She would give a phony name and phone number after talking with him and promising to meet him. She never did follow up on this plan.

Perhaps the scariest room in the entire dorm was the old shower and tub room. The lights were dim. Mildew reigned and water dripped from one of the faucets in a slow, tortuous rhythm. Alfred Hitchcock's newly released movie, *Psycho,* with its shower scene was terrifying. I took tub baths for about a month after seeing that movie. Kathy M. and Bonnie C. seemed to enjoy this room because of the acoustics. Both had beautiful singing voices. They would sing in harmony and sounded like the *Sound of Music.*

The funniest incident in the shower room was when Connie C. dyed her hair a raven black that she attempted to rinse off in the shower. Her body ended up covered with blotches of black. Her date was picking her up within the hour.

Life in the dorm had one favorite night. Wednesday night was Movie Night. A popular movie was shown, free of charge to all of the students. Everyone had to be ready for bed because the movie ended close to lights out at eleven p.m. All manner of curling rods, hair nets, bobby pin curls, colored bathrobes and funny looking slippers adorned us. Many cradled a bowl of popcorn.

The Connecting Tunnel

Before any freshman ever set foot inside the hospital or was even allowed to touch a living or deceased patient, she was told about the infamous tunnel that ran from the basement of the dormitory underground all the way to the hospital. This was the only way to get to the ground floor cafeteria in the hospital.

We learned to travel in groups or with at least one other classmate because it was a very spooky place. The overhead pipes were massive, numerous, noisy and dripping water all of the time. All of these pipes led to and from the hospital utilities. Lighting was dim.

The school strongly recommended that students not use the tunnel when alone. This posed a problem for students who slept in and were going to be late reporting for duty in the hospital. It was a real feat of dexterity to run through the tunnel while trying to attach a nursing cap to a frazzled head!

The Uniform

Measuring day for our uniforms arrived one fine day in January. The tape was wrapped around the waist and hung down to exactly twenty-six inches from the floor. One dark-colored stripe was on the left sleeve. A second stripe was added in the beginning of the second year and a third at the start of the third year. The starch content of the uniform could feed a family of twenty people. God forbid if one had to bend over to pick something up from the floor. It would feel like you were cut in half. They were hard to move in and were very irritating to the back and sides of the neck.

Our uniforms were pristine white and very professional looking. Everyone was eager for the hospital experiences. Rules were to be rigidly followed when wearing the uniform: hair must be off of the collar, no jewelry except a wrist watch with a second hand, minimal make-up, full length white cotton slips and nylons, white sweaters and spotlessly clean white nursing shoes. When on duty in the operating room and the obstetrics department, the student had to wear surgical garb.

Men Galore

The blue school bus arrived in front of Marian Hall three times a week with Elmer behind the wheel. He was responsible for transporting the students to Canisius College, an all-male institution. As soon as the bus doors closed, the singing began. Songs were belted out in fairly good harmony: "Scotch and Soda," "I'm Going to Wash that Man Right Out of My Hair," "Hit the Road Jack," "St. Peter Don't You Call Me Home," "Row, Row, Row Your Boat," " Hundred Bottles of Beer on the Wall," and "Oh, Bill, I Love You Still." The time passed quickly before the bus pulled into one of the parking lots on campus. Making sure that lipstick was on straight and that skirts were wrinkle free was done before getting off of the bus. Elmer seemed to enjoy the musical interludes.

On one fine day, we did the Bunny Hop from the Science building to the cafeteria, to the delight of the male students. There was a very large pool of males to date. The only competition was the students from the rival nursing school, the Sisters of Charity in Buffalo. Everyone was excited to be going to classes. Hours were spent the night before classes trying on various outfits and swapping clothes in the dorm.

My favorite class was chemistry, which was taught by a Jesuit priest who loved nurses. Father Joseph Muenzen promised that he would pass everyone in his class with a B grade as long as we showed up for class. Besides chemistry, he taught us how to build a still to make whiskey and how to make a perfect martini.

Dr. Stouter who gave us mountains of homework and frequent exams taught Anatomy and Physiology. Everyone thought that he was very cute when he turned red while teaching the male reproductive organs and their functions. Of course, there were a number of us who turned red as well. The class wasn't always lively. One day, Mary Lee S. fell asleep in class and fell into the aisle. Ouch!

Something should have been done about the elderly Jesuit priest who taught logic. Father Murray was deaf and almost blind. He had a difficult time pronouncing some of our names, such as Mumme and Wintermantel. When a student tried to correct him, it would turn into a shouting match between them. The whole class would start to laugh. This made the priest very mad. The class became stressful and not very informative.

Dr. Katherine Treanor taught the Physiology class. This class brought together the anatomy and physiology teachings through the dissecting of a dead cat. Two students who held their noses over the stinking mess shared the carcass. Our instructor was not pleased to find a sign tacked onto a coffin-like box holding the carcass that said, "Here Lies Poor Pussy Bouzer." This was Kathy M.'s kitty cat.

A real macho priest, Father Cantillon, taught sociology. He told us that a woman's menstrual period was her womb crying because there was no baby in it. Everyone with a womb dreaded going to his class.

Quite a debonair priest, Father Belmonte, taught microbiology. Microscopes and Petri dishes made organisms come alive. During our instruction, we had to prick our own finger and diagnose our blood type. A drop of our blood was smeared on a slide and viewed under a microscope. Emilie and I helped each other by obtaining the blood drop for each other and neither one of us fainted this time.

The sweetheart of all of the Jesuit teachers was the English teacher, Father Martin. Shy and gentle, he gave us a lot of homework but no one complained about it. Being from Niagara Falls, I was a loyal Niagara University Purple Eagles basketball fan and Father, naturally, was a loyal Canisius College Griffins basketball fan. We had some lively discussions about the two teams.

It took a lot of courage to walk into the lunchroom at Canisius. I was usually pushed by my classmates to be the first person to go into the room. As soon as my foot touched the floor, the jukebox started playing "Stairway to the Stars." We found out later that this was a stripper song.

Chapter Two
Second Semester, Freshman Year:
A.K.A. "We Survived"

Boot Camp

Courses continued at Canisius and in the basement classroom at Marian Hall. Fundamentals of Nursing intensified to include bed making a hospital bed without a patient in it. A quarter had to bounce off of the bottom sheet in order to pass the test. There were two hospital beds in the basement classroom-teaching laboratory. Each student had to sign up for hospital bed making 101, in the evening hours after eight p.m. The trick was to lie on the floor underneath the bed and pull the sheet with all of your strength to tighten the fabric. The bed would be examined by Sister Mary Claver the next day and graded.

After learning how to make a bed with a taut bottom sheet, we had to learn how to make a bed with a mannequin in it, posing as a patient. We named her Mrs. Chase or Mrs. Bedford. We had to make the bed without dumping the mannequin on the floor. In these nursing labs, we learned how to take an oral, axillary, and rectal temperatures, and blood pressures and pulses in various parts of the body. We practiced on each other except for the rectal temperature procedure. These sessions helped us build confidence and made us less anxious to try the procedures on live patients.

To liven up the class one day, Mary Lee climbed into one of the two beds and pretended to be Mrs. Chase. Sister didn't seem to notice and continued teaching the class. Rachel tried the same prank on Father Krupa as he was teaching a class on medical ethics. He smiled and didn't mind the prank one bit.

Good Drugs from Sister

If a student felt ill, she was to report to the Health Center, which was located on the first floor of Marian Hall, in a room almost directly across from the Housemother's domain. Sister Mary Claver was in charge of diagnosing and treating the ill student.

The line of sick students would either be sitting on the stairs or standing in front of Room 103, waiting for Sister to appear. We were a sorry looking group. She would take a quick health history, do a cursory physical examination and make a determination as to the seriousness of the illness. She would pass out appropriate medications and send us on our way. In my case, Sister gave me a medication that relieved the menstrual cramps that had plagued me since I was eleven years old. The cramps would disappear in a short period of time and I was able to return to my regular schedule. Years later, I found out that I had been given a potent pain medication.

The First Hospital Experience

The day had finally arrived. We were dressed in our stiffly starched uniforms and were to report to the hospital for an orientation to the hospital floors. We were divided into four groups for the clinical experiences for the next two and a half years. No nursing caps adorned our heads yet. The cap had to be ironed as well as starched.

A nursing school instructor gave simple assignments to each student. One day I was instructed to go into a patient's room and lower the side rail from his hospital bed. She meant, "lower it" and I thought she meant, "remove it." It took me a while to accomplish this task but I did it. When the instructor asked me if I had any trouble with the assignment, I offered her a handful of nuts, bolts and screws, like a priest offering up the holy host. The bed rail was leaning against the wall. The patient had slept through the entire process. The astonished instructor asked me how I had done it. I dutifully held up my "handy dandy" bandage scissors that I had used as a screwdriver.

My fingernails were broken and I had a few small nicks on my fingers. My wrist and arms hurt like heck.

A maintenance man had to be called to put the guardrail back on the bed. After looking things over, he had to ask me which bolt went where because it was too complicated for him to figure out. This simple lesson taught both the instructor and me how crucial clear communication is in nursing. The patient was not harmed, thank God, and neither was the bed!

Intensive Experiences Begin

All of our classes were in Marian Hall, in the basement. There would be no more Canisius College and the Big Blue Bus with Elmer behind the wheel. Makeup was forgotten and our clothing consisted of comfy combinations of unfashionable attire.

Every Friday, the students and their instructors invaded Mercy Hospital. As I delivered more hands-on care, I became more confident in completing assignments and keeping side rails attached to beds.

The Cap

The much-anticipated day came when we received our nursing caps. Our capping ceremony was held on Sunday, February 12, 1961. We had one dark stripe on our left shoulder sleeve of our snow-white nursing uniform, indicating that we had completed our first year successfully. Next came the beautiful navy blue cape with the bright red lining. The ceremony was held in the hospital chapel with our parents and other family members in attendance. The nuns held a small reception in Marian Hall afterwards.

The focus of the first year of study was Fundamentals of Nursing. The next two years were to be devoted to the clinical experiences in multiple fields of nursing. This would give us a well-rounded experience in which to find our personal niche to specialize in after graduation. Assignments were based on a forty-hour week inclusive of class and ward conference hours. For clinical rotations, we were alphabetically divided into four groups of approximately sixteen students. Students in each of these groups would band together for survival during their learning experiences and help one another in completing their assignments.

My First Medical Surgical Experience: The Bed Bath

The Medical-Surgical floor appeared massive to a first year nursing student. I felt overwhelmed to see so many patients with so many different diagnoses. It seemed to me that patients with all of the diseases I had studied were right in front of me, both sexes, and all ages and sizes. I was very nervous. I did not want to misinterpret my instructions again. That side rail incident still was an embarrassment to me.

My instructor gave me the task of giving a bed bath to an elderly lady in a fifteen-bed ward. I reviewed her chart, reading all of her diagnoses, and looked up all her medications. Feeling confident, I introduced myself to the patient but found her sleeping. I didn't know what to do, so I found my instructor and explained the problem.

"Of course, give the patient the bath even if she's sleeping," was her response. Off to the Utility Room to fill the large tub with warm water I went. The towels were fluffy, the soap sudsy and the lotion was therapeutic sounding.

I chatted cheerfully while washing my patient. The patient's arms were quite heavy to lift and wash. The most difficult task came when I had to turn the patient over on her side in order to wash her back. All of her limbs seemed to flop all over the place. I was exhausted afterwards. With a clean gown on the patient and fresh linens on the bed, I went to find my instructor for her inspection and approval. That's when everything went wrong.

"How long has the patient been like this?" asked my instructor.

I answered, "Remember when I asked you about giving a bath to a sleeping patient?"

My instructor looked very uncomfortable, and in a low voice she informed me that my patient had died.

I wasn't sure that I had heard her right, so in a loud voice I said, "Do you mean she died?"

She instructed me to notify the Head Nurse to call her doctor and family. Eventually, I was to call Central Service and ask for a morgue pack.

The First Injection

I practiced using a needle and syringe all week long in the nursing laboratory. Using sterile water, I carefully filled the syringe and injected it into an orange. Sister Mary Claver's voice echoed in my mind: "Now you take this patient, please. To give an intramuscular injection in the buttocks, bring their pajamas bottoms down. Make a sign of the cross on the buttock with an alcohol soaked cotton ball. Draw back your arm and aim for the inner aspect of the upper outer quadrant." Today would be the real McCoy on a real buttock to inject a prescribed medication.

With the instructor by my side, I had successfully drawn up a syringe full of the medication as prescribed by the physician. I had researched the medication and recited the purpose of the treatment and the side effects of the drug.

I placed the prepared syringe and an alcohol soaked cotton ball on a small tray and we both walked into the patient's room. I asked the man for his name and compared it to his wrist identification band. Everything checked out so this patient was the intended victim. I informed him that I was to give him a shot of medicine that his doctor had ordered.

I asked him to turn on to his right side and flex his leg towards his chest. I turned down the bed sheet and saw that he was wearing a hospital gown, not pajama bottoms. This gown was opened from the neck down, leaving a clear access to his butt.

I picked up the alcohol soaked cotton ball and made the sign of the cross on the butt. I left the cotton ball in place to mark the spot and picked up the syringe. I drew back my arm, removed the cotton ball with the other hand, and aimed the syringe at the bull's eye. I promptly froze.

The instructor firmly grabbed my wrist and guided my hand with a quick jab into the site. She mouthed the words "draw back" to me. This was done to make sure that the needle wasn't in a vein. It wasn't. I injected the medication and the patient didn't die, thank goodness.

Holy of Holies

As the nursing school was run by the Sisters of Mercy religious order, the spiritual life in the school was strict. After all, there could be a potential novice in the group of young ladies. We were encouraged to attend daily Mass and receive Holy Communion in the hospital's Chapel. If unable to be at Mass, we were encouraged to say prayers in the Chapel before we reported for hospital duty. Father Francis Krupa was the Chaplain at the hospital. He taught us medical ethics in our senior year of schooling. He was a kind, gentle man who seemed to have a good sense of humor.

The nun in charge of our religious lives posted a list of student names that were assigned to accompany Father as he gave Communion to the hospital patients. The problem was that this was at the ungodly hour of six-thirty a.m. Some forgot to go. Some simply ignored the assignment. Some tried to find someone else to take their place. No one wanted to get up at five-thirty, get dressed and walk through the spooky tunnel alone to the hospital Chapel to meet Father. Father didn't report any of the students who failed to show up. For this reason alone, we all thought the world of him.

Another part of our spiritual encouragement included a two-day retreat in our senior year. The retreat was held at the Mercy Retreat House on Delaware Avenue in Buffalo. Every senior class had to attend and no one was exempt. It was two days of absolute quiet, a time of soul searching and individual reflection. No talking was allowed, even at meals. These rules and regulations were pure torture for us. The two days meant time away from the stress and pressure of studying and learning nursing skills.

It was like a mini-vacation or so we thought. Wrong! Of course, this retreat was a fresh opportunity for some really good pranks by the greatest prankster of them all, Mumme. I fell prey to a few of her good-humored tricks.

The first one was banging my head on a statue of St. Jude that rested on my pillow as I crawled into bed on the first night. I literally saw stars. I silently screamed her name. I thought that I was prepared for more statues in my cot the next night. I carefully felt around the pillow and found nothing. Feeling safe, I got into bed, but found Mumme's idea of soul searching included short sheeting my bed. I found it difficult to forgive my classmate for a while.

Chapter Three
Junior Year: September 1961
One Stripe, Two Stripes

Clinicals

Mercy Hospital School of Nursing was a nursing diploma school, with a "hands on" focus in all practice areas. These included Medical, Surgical, Pediatrics, Nursery, Obstetrics, Operating Room, Surgical Recovery Room, the Emergency Room and the Out-Patient Department. Each experience was at Mercy Hospital and had its own instructor. The Psychiatric experience was at St. Vincent's Hospital in Harrison, New York, about thirty miles from New York City. In September of 1961, we began our journey into each of these areas.

What Is That Thing?

Our surgical instructor was a kind woman that helped us prepare to assist surgeons in the operating room. The instructor stood in front of a large tray covered with a white towel. She removed the towel to reveal numerous serialized surgical instruments. We had one week to memorize them and practice handling them with ease.

We were then led to a surgical observation area to view an operation in progress. I saw a pale green painted room with three people standing in front of a large white elevated object. There was a large red stain in the center of this object. It looked like a Bulls Eye. The instructor whispered, "You're witnessing a hemorrhoidectomy." I suddenly realized that the large lump was some one's rear end. I felt faint and wondered how I was going to survive this rotation.

At the learning laboratory in Marian Hall, Sister Mary Claver had numerous surgical instruments available for us to handle and memorize. Memorization, hand-eye coordination and concentration had to be 100 percent correct, along with maintaining sterile technique. This is where the knitters had it all over the rest of us. Knitters were used to knitting two and purling two with very sharp needles.

Monday through Thursday, we were assigned to observe operations after we had scrubbed in and suited up in sterile surgical garb. We saw how the surgical team worked in a synchronized rhythm to open a body orifice, repair or remove tissue and confidently reattach everything as before. We observed and assisted in many types of surgeries. I was fascinated to see what our internal organs looked like and how they were assembled in our body.

One of my classmates, Rachel, was observing a leg amputation when she was instructed to hold on to the leg while it was being removed. When it was successfully severed, she was told to place the leg on the operating table. She froze in place, holding the limb. The charge nurse had to step in and remove it. She was told to "snap out of it!"

A Huge Bowl of Jell-O

Each one of us was assigned to follow a patient through the entire surgical process, from being admitted to the hospital to discharge after a successful operation. It was my day to report to Admissions at the hospital to meet my assigned patient. My patient was a timid woman who looked at least eight months pregnant. She wasn't. Her distended abdomen was due to an ovarian tumor. She was single, lived on a farm, spoke very little English and appeared frightened. Her brother was with her during the Admissions process but left as soon as we got her settled in her hospital room.

I went out to the nursing station and started putting together her chart, which would include everything pertaining to this patient. I found the doctor's orders and filled out the necessary forms for laboratory tests and medications.

I went to bed before lights out that night, but didn't sleep very well due to nerves. I was at my patient's bedside at six a.m. to administer the ordered preoperative medications. I tried to calmly reassure the patient. Before I knew it, it was time to place the patient on a gurney and wheel her into the operating room. I left to scrub and dress for the operation.

The doctor and the surgical team, including the anesthesiologist were ready to operate. As soon as the anesthesiologist gave the surgeon permission to begin the operation, he turned to me and said "scalpel." I was quick on the draw and slapped the instrument into the palm of his hand, as taught. He grimaced and asked me to be less enthusiastic in the future. Her abdomen was carefully opened. I handed the instruments as the surgeon requested and tried to be less enthusiastic at all times.

The problem occurred when the size of the ovarian tumor was exposed, as it was massive. The surgeon yelled for a sterile bucket. Another nurse and I held retractors to pull the abdominal tissue back, so the doctor could access the tumor. The doctor had to extract it without rupturing it, so the contents could not wash into the entire abdominal cavity and causes a serious condition known as sepsis. This tumor could be cancerous as well. Another nurse brought in a sterile bucket and the juggling act began. Soon the doctor was able to plop the entire mass into the bucket, and everyone breathed a sigh of relief. The remainder of the surgery proceeded normally.

I helped transfer my patient to the Recovery Room where Miss C., the Head Nurse, reigned. While my patient slept, I took her blood pressure and pulse every fifteen minutes. I checked her abdominal dressing for any bleeding. Urinary output was recorded and the intravenous fluids were infusing at the prescribed rate. My patient was stable. Thank God!

My patient gradually woke up. I took her back to her assigned hospital room and took care of her the rest of the day. For the next seven days, I was at her bedside, giving her all of the postoperative care that was ordered by her doctor. The pathology report on the tumor was benign for cancer. I wheeled a very healthy looking woman to the front door of the hospital and said goodbye to her.

She gave me a shy wave as she got into her brother's truck to go home.

The entire experience made me feel like I was a finally a nurse.

Timing is Everything

Labor and Delivery was run like a smooth machine under the direction of a midget nun, Sister Mary Jean Baptist. When the baby census was low, Sister had a habit of turning on a light in front of a picture of the Holy Family, to encourage admissions.

On my first day of clinical, I reported for duty to one of the floor nurses, who was overworked and in a big hurry. She literally shoved me into a patient's room and told me to stay with the patient until she returned. She instructed me to time the patient's contractions, how long they were as well as how often they happened. Not knowing what else to do, I introduced myself to the patient. This was her third pregnancy. She had two daughters at home and she and her husband were hoping for a boy. They had picked out a name already, Joseph. Her husband was at home taking care of their two daughters. During our conversations, I was aware of her panting and facial grimacing.

I casually checked my two-handed wristwatch and noted the time and lengths of her contractions. This went on for about an hour and still the floor nurse was nowhere to be seen. I was no expert, but I soon realized that this lady was going to deliver her baby right in the bed if I didn't get help quickly. I pried my hand out of the woman's death grip and went in search of a real nurse. I looked everywhere but I couldn't find one.

Suddenly, the nurse who had sent me into the patient's room came out of another room. I told her what was happening to my patient. The seasoned nurse told me to get back to the patient right away and not bother her with trivial nonsense. She said that this lady would not be ready for delivery for at least a few more hours. She was busy assisting with another delivery and didn't have time to check my patient.

I went back to my lady to find her with her knees bent and she seemed to be pushing something. Pure panic! I remembered the movie *Gone with the Wind* and that famous remark of "I don't know nothin' bout birthin' no babies!"

Suddenly, the doctor arrived and shouted for a gurney. I ran like the devil and brought one into the room while he was examining his patient. We got her on the gurney and began wheeling her towards the delivery room but we didn't make it. Baby Joseph was delivered in the hall on the gurney. The doctor's suit was rather soiled, but it was a happy ending for everyone.

When Sister found out what had happened, the seasoned nurse was severely reprimanded for leaving a green student nurse in charge of a patient with a fully dilated cervix. She checked the gurney to see if there was a Lippe's Contraceptive Loop lying on it but found none to add to her shoebox collection.

I was the primary care nurse for this patient and for baby Joseph for the next five days. What a joy it was to give the young mother a refreshing bed bath and to do the post-delivery assessments. Before long, I wheeled her down to the nursery to see her newborn baby. Joseph had been given a bath as well. His head was cylinder shaped, as pushing out of that little hole mashed his soft cranial bones, but in a few months, his head would be finely shaped. Both mom and I praised and cooed our love for him through the nursery glass. For five days, I took care of Joseph in the nursery and took him to see his mother at the scheduled time. She had decided not to breastfeed. Bottle fed babies were brought to their mothers every four hours for feeding. The nursery got quite noisy near feeding time.

It was a happy day when I wheeled both mother and baby to the hospital's front door and said good-bye. Her husband was at the curb with the car door opened for them. It turned out that he owned a pizzeria in town. He generously offered free pizzas to me and to my friends in payment for taking such good care of his wife and baby son.

The most frightening thing I experienced was witnessing a placenta previa. The poor woman was in mortal danger of bleeding to death because the placenta had separated from the uterine wall. I was asked to help the floor nurse insert a Foley catheter into the patient before she went into surgery for an emergency Caesarean Section. It was impossible to insert because of all of the blood coming from the vagina.

After we got the patient on a gurney, I was instructed to stay behind and wash the bed down with an antiseptic solution. I found out later that the woman made it through surgery and both she and her baby were doing fine. She was receiving blood transfusions to replace what she lost. I was so relieved that all was well with her and her little one.

A Captive Audience

Yolanda was given the very important assignment of teaching young mothers how to give a baby bath. She was nervous about it, but had practiced on a baby doll at the teaching laboratory at Marian Hall all week. She had the routine down to all the fine points.

She looked around the room and saw a group of attentive mothers eager to learn, as she realized that all of them were older than her. Yolanda knew that they had nowhere to go once she closed the door. Before their arrival, she had gone to the hospital nursery and had chosen the largest baby to use in the demonstration. His mother was honored that her son had been chosen and readily signed the consent form giving Yolanda permission.

Baby Boy was lying wide-awake in his bassinet, waving his little arms around like an excited maestro.

Yolanda explained the bath steps, and the importance of testing the bath water for the proper temperature with your elbow. After everything was prepared, Yolanda undressed the baby and gently laid him on a fluffy towel and began to give him a sponge bath. She soon found out that bathing a living, squirming baby was totally different from bathing a doll. The hard part occurred when she washed his hair. She rolled him up in a towel like a little cannelloni, and holding him like a football close to her chest, proceeded to wash his hair over the basin.

Baby Boy didn't like this idea one bit and began bellowing loudly for help.

Trying to talk over the noise was tricky. Yolanda laid him back down on the towel and unwrapped him. She was about to put a clean, cloth diaper on him when he urinated straight in her face. With urine dripping from her chin, she explained the wise decision to hold a washcloth over the penis until the diaper is in place.

From the response of the mothers, her class was a success. As for Yolanda, she was absolutely exhausted. Who would have thought that an eight-pound baby could feel like eight hundred pounds of wiggling, squiggling Jell-o? Her instructor gave her an excellent grade for professionalism and preparation.

Mixing It Up

The rotation to nursery duty was thought to be a vacation for students. It was soon evident that the vacation was not to be. New deliveries were constantly arriving, like travelers in an airport. These new arrivals had to be thoroughly examined by the nurses, and their tiny heels pricked to obtain blood samples to test for inherited diseases. These little travelers were exhausted from their stressful journey into the world.

The students were expected to do many things all at once. One responsibility was to prepare the formula mixtures for the babies, and was done under sterile conditions. The exact amount of full strength formula was mixed with the exact amount of sterile water. The student had to instruct the new mothers on breastfeeding as well. One day, a mother began screaming while her baby was feeding at her breast. Her baby was born with two tiny teeth that had sunk into the mothers' nipple and literally drew blood. A veteran nursery nurse was able to release the baby by depressing the suction from the baby's hold on the mother.

Mother and baby were carefully matched by checking their identification wristband with the baby's ankle identification band. One mother had no trouble in identifying her baby boy.

He had the largest nose ever seen on an infant's face. Jimmy Durante would've been proud!

Everyone knew when feeding time was approaching by the increasing wails of hungry babies. The crying started with one infant. Soon, a second infant would join in. Before long, the entire nursery sounded like a screaming contest between opposing sport teams. Every four hours, bassinets were lined up for takeoff to the mother's hospital rooms. Time passed quickly for us, as we prepared formula for the next feedings. After an hour spent with their moms, the babies were brought back to the nursery.

In between feeding times, the mothers and their visitors would come to the nursery window and coo to their baby through the glass. If a baby were crying, we would pick the baby up and rock it to sleep. Sometimes, the mother would witness this comforting and be given permission to enter the nursery and hold her baby. All of the babies were kept in the nursery at night, except for the breastfed babies, in order to allow the mothers a good night sleep. The average length of hospitalization after delivery was one week, and the mother was not allowed out of bed for the first two days.

After completing the nursery clinical, the student nurses had a new respect for the nursery nurses. They were truly whirling dervishes!

The Fix-Up

I was dating a very nice young man from Niagara Falls, Joe Weber. Joe had passed Sister Mary Ethel's scrutiny with flying colors. He was a student at Niagara University and had a charming personality. Joe had a lot of handsome friends who were looking to date lovely ladies. He asked me if there were any student nurses at Mercy who would be interested in a blind date. It didn't take me long to find several friends who would love to meet these young men. I introduced my dear friend, Emilie to Dan, Yolanda to Kerns, and Rachel to James. Through Dan, Margie C. met her future husband, Bill. I became Mrs. Weber a year after graduation.

The Big Apple with Nuts

I had wanted to go to New York City to take acting lessons after high school. My mother absolutely forbade it! No daughter of hers was going to that rotten apple of a city. Little did we both know that I would end up thirty miles from that city for three months during the summer of 1962.

Our clinical group was assigned to an affiliation at a psychiatric facility in Westchester County near Rye Town. It meant that I could take the commuter train into the big city on my days off to shop and be a tourist.

I flew for the first time from Buffalo to New York City with a group of fellow student nurses, including my dear friend, Emilie. A friendly stewardess walked up and down the airplane aisle and handed out free cigarette samples to everyone. Although some of us didn't smoke, we took them anyway. We thought that they might come in handy someday. Once on the ground, we piled into a limousine for the ride to the psychiatric facility. Our lives would be forever changed because of this rotation.

Our Gothic Psych Rotation Begins

The limousine made a left hand turn and drove down a long driveway that was over shadowed with beautiful trees and flowering bushes. It stopped in front of a Gothic building that looked like it belonged in the book, *Wuthering Heights* or Ravenhearst Manor. This was to be our living quarters. Emilie and I shared a room on the top floor and for an extra five dollars we bought a key to our closet. We placed our valuables in our suitcases and kept the door locked. The other visible building across the driveway was modern, standing three stories tall. This building was the hospital for the acutely ill. There were several other *Wuthering Heights* buildings scattered through a heavily wooded area behind our living quarters. These buildings housed the chronically ill patients. A lot of these patients were ill members of the clergy hidden away from society.

Burgling Nuns

At the end of the first day, Emilie and I were exhausted and fell into our beds at an early hour. I awoke in the middle of the night to hear Emilie speaking to someone in our room. I rolled over and got the shock of my life to see two nuns going through our dresser drawers with flashlights. I shouted at them to stop what they were doing and to get out of our room. They quickly scurried away. When we told the Housemother about this intrusion the next morning, she informed us that the nuns were searching for stolen drugs. Odd, since we hadn't even been in the hospital or had exposure to medications yet. The excuse sounded lame to me. This was the first of many weird happenings that I would encounter during this rotation.

Words Our Mothers Never Taught Us

The first day of my student orientation began in the basement of the modern-looking psychiatric building. While touring the building, I noticed a nurse approaching us. She was pushing a woman in a wheelchair down the long hall. As soon as the patient saw us, she began screaming obscenities that I had never heard before. "You sluts, fucking bitches, you cunts, mother fuckers, assholes!"

My eyes and mouth fell open with shock until the instructor reprimanded me for my uncontrolled facial expressions. Snapping my mouth shut, I was told that this type of behavior was nothing unusual and I was to hide my feelings from patients at all times. The patients, I was told, responded to our reactions and would keep doing certain behaviors in order to upset staff. Well, it worked!

The head instructor, Miss Godek, taught the afternoon classes. She had a whiny voice and a habit of leaning into your face as she spoke. She would stare directly into my eyes and ask personal questions that were completely unsettling. In these classes, we were taught the various mental illnesses and their treatments. These were very informative and, at the same time, frightening.

Electroshock Therapy

In the first week of my clinical, I was instructed to take a patient down to the basement laboratory for a blood test. The woman was cooperative but seemed frightened. I soon understood her apprehension. She was anxious that her "blood test" might actually turn into an electroshock therapy (ECT) session. ECT was often used to treat patients with severe depression.

I'll never forget the day I observed an ECT session. A fully conscious female patient was placed on a bed while two nurses applied wrist restraints, and then inserted a rubber mouth plate to prevent her from biting her tongue. A rubber strap was placed around her head, with electrodes on either side of her temples. I watched in horror as the doctor flipped a switch, delivering jolts of electricity, thereby shocking the poor patient. It seemed like the doctor held his finger down on the switch forever. The patient's body began to stiffen and convulse, and the convulsions seemed to go on and on. After the convulsions ended, the patient went into a deep sleep, which lasted for four hours.

When the patient woke up, I helped return her to her room and found it odd that she had no memory of what had happened. These ECT sessions, along with insulin shock treatment, medications and psychotherapy, were the gold-standard treatments of the 60s, all with the goal of returning in-patients to a normal life.

Nuns and Priests: Our Psych Patients

Work on the female patient floor soon became routine for me as my nursing skills improved. The women played cards and watched television until bedtime, with sleeping pills for everyone. One thing that began to occur to me was that these poor souls had no visitors, even on Sundays, the day for family and friends to visit. I discussed this sad situation with my colleagues and they noticed the same thing. After a short while, we came to realize that several of our patients were nuns and priests dressed in civilian clothing. This was a huge shock for Catholic nursing students!

A Padded Cell, The Homicidal Priest, and More

After the female acute care experience, I was transferred to the acute men's care floor. As soon as I arrived, I was assigned to go to a room and stay with a patient. My key opened the door and I saw a completely white room with thick padding on every wall. A man in a black suit was lying on the floor. He appeared to be in a deep sleep. I cautiously bent down and took his pulse. The rate was very low but he was very much alive. I didn't know what else to do.

After a few minutes, I wandered around the room and leaned against the wall closest to my patient and kept careful watch. He began to stir after an hour and gradually opened his eyes.

I walked over to him and told him my name and asked him for his. He looked up at me and said, "I must be in heaven. Look at you in your white robe and white halo. An angel!"

As I backed away, an orderly unlocked the door and took over the watch for me. Apparently, this man was in the Quiet Room in case he went through violent "delirium tremors" from alcohol withdrawal. Thank goodness for the white student uniform and cap! He was in awe of an angel (me) and wouldn't attempt to tear off her wings!

Prior to my duty on the men's floor, the reputation of an alcoholic and homicidal priest was well known. He had the ability to "elope," which was another word for escaping. He would walk into the nearby town to a saloon and get rip-roaring drunk. The police would bring him back to the psychiatric center and the staff would have to deal with him in his homicidal state. The patients were deathly afraid of him. Well, wouldn't you know? He was returned to us one night when I was on duty.

Another time, Father had been missing since early afternoon, with plenty of time to get drunk. My only consolation was that I had an Orderly on duty with me. I was praying that the police wouldn't find him until the wee hours of the night when I wasn't on duty. But no! I received a phone call from the Supervisor informing me of his imminent return about nine p.m.

By this time, the other thirty-five patients were ready for bed, pajamas on, and having their snacks. Sleeping pills, psychotics, and other medications were poured and ready to be dispensed at ten p.m.

I turned to tell the orderly about Father's arrival, only to be told by the patients that he had left the floor again. What a holy Houdini! I called the Supervisor but she told me to handle the priest as best I could when he returned, because she couldn't send any extra help.

I put my thinking cap on and had an idea! I asked the patients to set up all of the card tables and get the playing cards out. My own father loved to play cards when he was drinking and I thought that this might be true with "Father Houdini." I set out a lot of snacks and cold sodas to drink. I tried to look competent and in control so as not to cause panic among the patients.

No sooner were things arranged when Father was returned to the floor in all of his glory. He stood at least 6'4" and weighed well over 250 pounds. An unlit cigarette was dangling out of his mouth.

"Give me some matches, you, right now," he growled at me.

Everyone knew that patients were not allowed to have matches, only staff people. We would light their cigarettes for them.

"Father, I'll light your cigarette for you," I said, following the rules.

"God damn it, girl! Give me those matches!" His eyes said I'd better obey.

I handed him the matches...so much for following the rules. There was murder in his eyes and I did not want to be his victim!

After he lit his cigarette, I was able to steer him into the recreation room and sat him down at a card table. The other patients had to be coaxed into joining us because they were afraid of this man. I started a card game with Father.

He won all of the games. He smoked a pack of Pall Malls and drank ten ginger ales. Soon, that book of matches was almost empty. A few of the patients wandered back to the safety of their rooms for the night, happy that their nurse had not been murdered. When the night nurse came on duty, he was still playing cards. I hadn't given out the ten p.m. medications yet and explained the reason why. After giving out the pills, I left, glad to be a problem-solver and to be alive.

There were other male patients that I still can remember vividly. One was a young man from Hungary. He had witnessed the Hungarian Uprising in 1956, six years prior. He was diagnosed as a schizophrenic, and I wondered what effect witnessing so much violence might have had on such a young mind. Blond hair, blue eyes, this very handsome young man was sadly affected for life with a very debilitating psychiatric illness.

Another young man was admitted with a drug addiction. We were supposed to watch him carefully and search his room for drugs when he wasn't present. Day after day, I found nothing in his dresser drawers or bedding.

But one day, as I turned to leave his room, I put my hand in a recessed wall opening and felt melted wax. Perplexed, I stepped back and turned around. That innocent-looking teaspoon lying on his bed stand wasn't so innocent looking anymore. Somehow, he had purloined matches, a candle, a spoon and drugs.

The Night Shift in Wuthering Heights

With only one more week left in this hellhole, Sister discovered that two students, Joanne P. and I, had not worked the night shift. How tragic is that? The dreaded night shift was to be spent in the chronic female ward, remotely located deep in the woods of the old gothic building that gave me the creeps.

With a flashlight borrowed from the Housemother, Joanne and I walked together through the dark and lonely woods. We felt like two Little Red Riding Hoods and were on the alert for the Big Bad Wolf. On duty, we got our nursing report on forty elderly female patients who needed physical nursing care as well as psychiatric care. In order to get through the night shift, we decided to split up the ward into two sections. If either one of us needed help, we'd be there for each other. The night duty was harder on the chronic unit. We had to start getting the patients ready for the day at five a.m.

One patient would continually remove all of her clothing and walk around carrying a baby doll. Some patients wandered around, crying out, some screaming and hitting themselves.

I found it really difficult to care for them. We worked the night shift for five straight nights. On the last day, we walked back to the dormitory with relief in our hearts and weariness in our steps. We had survived the night shift and also this mad place, and were finally going home to Buffalo and Niagara Falls.

Thumbing Our Way for a Free Ride and Other Off-Duty Tales

Not all of our psychiatric experience was doom and gloom. I certainly had some fun times. Rye Town Beach was nearby for sunbathing and we all found a cheap way to reach it: hitchhiking! My mother lectured me on the dangers of hitchhiking, but, we were brave, broke, and we had a system all worked out.

There were always four or five of us who stuffed our bathing suits in a beach bag and hit the road. A coin was tossed or someone volunteered to be the main attraction to the driver. The rest us would hide behind a tree and wait for the victim to stop his car. He would think that he had gotten lucky to pick up a very pretty girl all by herself. The bait always worked.

Once he stopped the car and offered our classmate a ride, the rest of us would climb into the car with her. The reaction was usually funny to see. Surprise followed by laughter. Most of us ended up with dark, rich tans by the end of that summer.

Besides Rye Town Beach, I joined my classmates for an outing to nearby New York City or "Freedom Land." On days off, we attacked the garment district with a vengeance, looking for the latest fashions at reasonable prices. The Statue of Liberty, Ellis Island, the Empire State building, and the United Nations were all graced by our visits. Those who could afford it went to plays on Broadway. That was my dream: to be on Broadway, on stage and not in the audience.

On those rare occasions when Emilie and I had the same day off, we would walk to the small town near the hospital and go to the bank. My mother had stressed the importance of safely banking the little amount of money I had brought with me. Whenever I needed cash, we'd walk to town. Afterwards, we'd go to the local soda joint and have something to eat. It felt great to be away from our psych responsibilities and be just two carefree young ladies out for the afternoon.

Emilie had given herself a home permanent the day before our walk. The day was overcast and it looked like rain, but we decided to walk into town anyway. No sooner had we walked a few blocks than Mother Nature let loose with a heavy downpour of cold rain. We started to run but there was nowhere to go. We were thoroughly soaked in no time.

Suddenly, a station wagon pulled up beside us, and the driver offered us a ride. His wife was in the front seat and his two kids were in the back seat. We gratefully got into the back seat with his children. Instantaneously, Emilie's hair gave off puffs of a chemical aroma that made eyes water and noses stuff up. Despite the rain, we all lowered the car windows. I think that kindly man broke the speed limit driving into town in order to drop us off as soon as possible.

I spotted a Laundromat near the bank and ran for the door. We put money into a large dryer and stripped off as many of our wet clothes as possible without being arrested for indecent exposure. Emilie's hair still stank to high heaven, but it curled beautifully.

The Housemother From Hell

I haven't mentioned the Housemother from Hell yet. I've been saving her for last. A large woman, the Housemother sat at her desk at the end of the long entrance hall in the dormitory. Her assistant, a tiny woman, could be seen lurking behind the mailbox area, poking her face out only to watch a conversation between the Housemother and students.

The Mother, a dour, unsmiling woman, reigned supreme. She controlled the phones, mail, messages and student life in general. She seemed delighted to tell me that I had no mail, no messages, and no news either. I would want to go back to the mailroom to double check for my mail from home, but her assistant was always back there, hovering.

On my last day at the hospital, I was astounded to see the Housemother and her assistant being arrested by the FBI and led away in handcuffs to be placed in the back seat of a police car. My mother had been smart in having me put my money in the bank. These two women had been stealing the money and stamps that were mailed by family members to their daughters.

Throughout the past year, Sister Mary Ethel and the FBI had been working together to find proof of their thievery. After receiving multiple complaints from parents about the missing cash that had been sent to their daughters, Sister suspected that someone was stealing mail. She contacted the FBI and they organized a sting operation to catch the thief. The student nurses who helped carry out the operation were completely undercover.

To this day, no one knows who assisted in the scheme. Both the Housemother from Hell and her sneaky assistant were arrested on federal charges of mail theft. I remember hoping that they got long jail sentences.

Get Me Out of Here!

In my zeal to leave that place, I packed my suitcase two weeks before I left. All I had to do was work the last night shift with Joanne, eat a hasty breakfast and change into travel clothes. My boyfriend, Joe and his friend Dan who was dating Emilie, were driving to Harrison to take us home to Niagara Falls. It was late August and the weather was hot and humid. Because Joe had no air-conditioning in the station wagon, Emilie and I decided to wear shorts and sleeveless tops during the long drive home.

However, the nuns strictly forbade this type of attire. Rule #1: Skirts and modest tops at all times when out of uniform. Mercy Hospital School of Nursing had a similar rule as well. I came up with the brilliant idea that we could cover our outfits with a long trench coat, buttoned up tight. Who could guess what was underneath the coat? Guess again? Who would even think of wearing a coat in 90-degree weather with no hint of rain in the sky?

But suddenly I heard her. "Miss O'Connor, come here," the Director of Nurses said sternly. "Open that coat so that I can see what you're wearing underneath it."

I complied; Sister gasped.

I pleaded, "Sister, the ride home is over eight hours long and the weather is so hot. I can't change now!"

"You're refusing to change your outfit?"

"Yes, Sister."

"Well! This violation of the rules has earned you and your friend a demerit on your report card. I intend to tell Sister Mary Ethel about your insubordination."

Emilie and I removed our coats and walked to the car with our heads held high. I asked Joe to hit the gas and get us out of there. For a short distance, we followed the police cars that held our Housemother and her assistant imprisoned in a cruiser. Those cars veered off towards New York City, while we shuffled off to Buffalo.

Joe pulled up to my home on Pierce Avenue nine hours later. My parents were thrilled to have me back home and that night, I climbed into my own bed and cried. I had survived the experience and had matured by leaps and bounds.

Chapter Four
Senior Year:
Three Stripes and I'm Out

Ready For Duty

After spending a glorious two days at home, I returned to Marian Hall. Harrison and the psychiatric rotation were behind me and I was ready to go into my third and final year of schooling. From September of 1962 to June of 1963, I would complete my clinical experiences and take the (much feared) New York State Board of Education Nursing Examinations. I felt older and wiser.

Marian Hall was quiet, as the last clinical group was at Harrison. They would be spending the next three months with Miss Godek and her crew of misfits. They would be spared the pleasure of meeting the evil Housemother and her lurking assistant. Their mail would be safe from prying eyes and sticky fingers. The biggest loss to them would be missing out on Rye Town Beach and returning home with a golden tan.

During my final year of training, I had clinical experiences in Pediatrics, the Emergency Room, Community Health Nursing, and Triage Nursing and then, expanded Medical-Surgical nursing.

I observed the Head Nurse on a hospital floor to learn her responsibilities to the patients, staff, and attending physicians. After "shadowing" her for several days, I "took over" as Head Nurse. She was by my side every minute of the shift, so I could ask advice and seek her guidance when needed.

I also worked with registered nurses and had specific assignments, such as pouring medications for the entire floor of forty or more patients, giving wound care, and other medical treatments. Our instructors, who were always by our side or were readily available if we needed them, supervised all of these experiences.

This final year would truly make or break me. The experiences were intense, frustrating, and rewarding, all at the same time. I wanted to be a professional nurse who was thoroughly prepared and ready for duty and I was getting there!

Patty Cake, Patty Cake

The moment I stepped off the hospital elevator onto the pediatric floor, I was greeted by screaming, yelling, and shouting little voices. It sounded like pure mayhem. Phones were ringing and the nurses looked frantic to me.

I reported to the Head Nurse and was told that I could find our nursing instructors in the large conference room. Our two instructors looked calm and organized. By this time in our senior year, we were all confident in our nursing care for adults, but these little creatures, from newborn to age eighteen, opened a whole new world of care for us.

I cringed as I thought of giving an intramuscular injection to a tiny baby. Oral medications were given through bottles or feeding tubes. Intravenous solutions were given in veins via "cut downs" in their tiny ankles or little scalp veins. I felt totally unprepared...and I was!

The pediatric unit was filled to the brim with acutely ill infants and children. I could barely walk around a room without bumping into high-gated cribs holding little people.

One of our assignments was to compare the childhood textbook illnesses that we had learned in class with the actual diseases that we were seeing for the first time.

One infant, in particular, received a lot of attention. Student nurses and resident physicians entered the newborn infant's room and removed the little one's diaper to inspect the genitalia. The poor baby was born with a condition known as hermaphrodites, where a child is born with both male and female external genitalia. This condition was very rare. Surgery was soon scheduled for removal of one of the organs.

We were assigned to night duty on pediatrics for one full week. The floor was generally quieter at night, but still just as busy for the nursing staff. I cared for a six-week-old infant with whooping cough. He was kept in strict isolation in a croup tent filled with moist cold air, which helped reduce respiratory passages swelling. It was my job to keep the ice fresh by refilling the bin every hour on the hour. The poor little one had contracted the communicable disease from one of his siblings who hadn't been immunized for the disease. His prognosis for recovery was not good.

By the end of my pediatric rotation, I knew that this was one area of nursing that I would avoid. I became too emotionally involved with my patients and could barely stand to witness their suffering.

As part of my pediatric rotation, I was sent to a day care center in Buffalo to observe how the infants and toddlers were cared for. Emilie and I got on the city bus on the corner of Choate Avenue and Abbott Road in our student nurse uniform and red cape and cap.

The bus dropped us off close to the Guardian Angels Day Care on Delaware Avenue. We spent a delightful day observing the staff interacting with their small charges, but we didn't have to change a dirty diaper, burp a baby or wipe up sticky faces.

Code Blue and Code Red

The Emergency Room rotation was a time of simple observation and helping out when needed. Mercy Hospital's Emergency Room was a constantly busy place, with comings and goings of injured and ill people arriving for treatment. I felt that this was the department for me, as the adrenaline rush hit me in anticipation of the next patient arriving. We were expected to observe all three shifts in order to get the full experience of triage first hand.

The night that I was assigned to observe was a very busy one. There had been a serious car accident involving a husband and his wife. The wife had been driving her husband home from a local bar (probably our favorite bar, Mischler's) and lost control of the car when her husband suddenly grabbed the wheel. They crashed into a telephone pole. I was instructed to stay with the obviously inebriated husband while the doctor examined his wife. She was the most seriously injured. The doctor sent her to surgery immediately for internal bleeding and a possible fractured hip.

I watched my male patient moan and snore until he suddenly woke up and asked me, "Where is my beautiful wife?"

"She's being taken care of by the doctor and nurses. Just relax," I said, "and close your eyes and rest."

He obeyed, closing his right eye, but I noticed he did not close his left eyelid. On closer inspection, I realized that he didn't have an eyelid that was attached. Gosh!

Then I saw that his one arm was a lot shorter than the other arm. There was a visible bulge in the upper arm, under his bloody shirtsleeve. It occurred to me that he must have a compound fracture of the arm. That bulge was probably the humerus bone that had snapped in two and was poking through his skin.

The man was a physical mess but would recover from his injuries with little side effects if the doctor could find his eyelid. After a long wait, the doctor entered the cubicle and began treating his injuries. Surgical repair would have to wait until my patient was sober.

The doctor began to examine the man's facial injuries. Believe it or not, he found the missing eyelid in the man's hair. It seemed like the doctor spent hours suturing multiple facial lacerations.

Knock, Knock…Who's There?

As part of my clinical experience, I was assigned to shadow a community health nurse for one day. Mercy had a contract with the Visiting Nurses Association (VNA) of Buffalo.

Even though the nurse had a car from the agency, the student could not ride with her because of insurance reasons. This meant the bus for us! After many phone calls to find out the address and time to meet the nurse, I checked the bus schedule, and calculated the closest drop off point to the patient's home.

I remember the glances from the other bus riders as I sat in my seat wearing my white starched uniform, navy blue cape, and white nylons with white nursing shoes. I carefully held my white student-nursing cap in a clear plastic bag on my starched lap. Because it was nearing Halloween, I like to think that my fellow bus riders thought that I was on my way to a Halloween party in the middle of the afternoon.

My trip took a full hour of bus travel, then a bus transfer and more travel before I found the right apartment building in downtown Buffalo. I rang the security bell at the front door and was buzzed in after being told to take the elevator to the top floor. I knocked on the apartment door which was opened by a hunched over elderly lady. Barely able to look me in the eye, she directed me to a back bedroom where I found the visiting nurse.

After introductions, the nurse asked me to assist her in giving the patient personal care. I quickly found out that this was nothing like giving a hospital bath where the necessary supplies were "Central Service" supplied and completely ready for use.

The elderly woman had given the nurse an assortment of materials for the bed bath. The patient had suffered a stroke and was paralyzed on his left side and had impaired speech.

"All right, Miss," the VNA nurse said, "you can help me give the bath by first washing your hands?"

We then worked together and had the patient bathed and dressed in no time. We changed the bed linens and returned all of the supplies to their proper places.

During this whole bathing experience, we were able to assess the man's skin for any signs of breakdown, which could lead to the development of bedsores. The nurse had taken his vital signs before I had arrived, but left the room to talk to his wife about bowel and bladder habits, medications, dietary intake, and diet adherence.

I was surprised to see the nurse then actually opened up their refrigerator to see what food items were in there. She opened their food pantry to see what food supplies were on the shelves. She then asked the wife a lot of questions about her own health and took her vital signs as well. The entire visit lasted about an hour.

The nurse asked me if I had planned on going to the next home with her. That meant I'd have to take another bus to get there because it was too far away to walk. The nurse was kind enough to excuse me and sent me on my way.

When I got back to Marian Hall, I decided that I didn't like community health nursing and wouldn't go into that field of nursing after graduation. From all of the clinical experiences so far, the Emergency Room held the winning ticket.

Dialing 911

The day had arrived for Dr. John McCabe, our Medical Director of Student Health, to teach our senior class the art of triage at the scene of an accident. Triage is the process of determining the priority of patients' treatments based on the severity of their condition. The doctor was very dramatic in describing the triage process and what nurses were expected to do in the case of emergencies.

The class was held in the two-tiered classroom in the basement of Marian Hall. With Mrs. Chase, the mannequin, looking on from her hospital bed, the doctor called on ten of my classmates to step forward as "accident victims of a bus crash" and lie down on the floor. He walked around them and placed 3x5 index cards on their bodies, indicating their trauma injuries.

None of us were aware that we were all actively participating in a planned drama of a great catastrophe.

When the accident victims were settled on the floor, Dr. McCabe called on six of my classmates to administer triage to the victims. There was a lot of laughter until Dr. McCabe regained control of his laughing students.

But he suddenly lost control when he spilled a bottle of Mercurochrome on the floor. All of us, including the doctor, panicked. Sister Mary Claver would tell Sister Mary Ethel about the unsightly stain on the floor and blame the student nurses. We would be severely punished in some way if we couldn't remove it.

Dr. McCabe got down on his knees and scrubbed away at the spot with Ajax as hard as he could. One of my classmates joined in. Everyone held their breath until the red splotch faded to a tiny pink dot. Apparently the doctor was afraid of the nuns too! Someone had the foresight to take a picture of Dr. McCabe cleaning the floor with Ajax and the photo made it into our yearbook.

The triage lesson went well and we all learned a lot. This experience fit like a hand and glove for me with my emergency room affiliation. I was hooked!

Just Say No to Sex!

During the three years of nurses training, sexually transmitted diseases and birth control methods were never mentioned or, God forbid, taught. After all, Mercy Hospital School of Nursing was a Catholic institution. We would just have to find out for ourselves about this topic after we graduated.

Sister Mary Jean Baptist, from the Labor and Delivery Unit was famous for shaking her shoebox full of Lippes Loops at us. A Lippes Loop was a small T-shaped device inserted into the uterus as a form of long-acting birth control. Sister did not fully explain the purpose of the Lippes Loop. We all thought that she was a little loopy for collecting these loops.

The school's strict rules and regulations on moral conduct and decorum for students were pretty much ignored by all. A popular lover's lane was Choate Avenue outside the dorm.

We would park with our boyfriends on this street before walking into Marian Hall before curfew. Some necking and kissing went on in the parked cars. We suspected that the nuns living in the convent across the street might have been peeking through their windows at us. The convent was directly across the street from Marian Hall. What an unholy sight for them to see!

Hello Fidel and Mr. Khrushchev

The date was October 16, 1962. I had completed my shift on "Big Surg" (the surgical floor) at the hospital and I was exhausted. All I wanted to do was change out of my uniform and put on comfortable clothing before going to dinner. I debated whether to take a short nap or study for the Nursing State Boards.

None of these things happened. When I got off of the elevator on the third floor of Marian Hall, I heard the television blaring from the lounge. I looked in and saw my friends were crowded around the television.

Walter Cronkite was talking about Cuba in a very serious voice. The Russians, with Cuba's cooperation, had transported nuclear missiles from their homeland to Cuba. These missiles were in striking distance of American shores and cities. Perhaps they could even reach Harrison and Miss Godek!

President John F. Kennedy had issued a severe warning to both Cuba's Fidel Castro and Russia's Khrushchev, ordering the removal of the missiles. He ordered a naval "quarantine" surrounding the Cuban island to prevent further missiles being delivered by Russian ships.

All of us thought of our relatives, friends and boyfriends in the military service. They would be directly involved in defending our country from attack.

My older brother had served in World War II, another brother had served in Germany, and my boyfriend was in ROTC at Niagara University. I felt strongly that I should step up to the military plate and enlist as a registered nurse. I considered asking Sister Mary Ethel if I could take the Nursing State Boards early.

The next three days were days of high anxiety for us all. The country was on high alert for a possible nuclear attack.

The world escaped nuclear war in October 1962, largely because of the prudence of Kennedy and the belated actions of Khrushchev. I'm sure that Kennedy and Khrushchev both recognized that, once things started, it would be very hard to keep any crisis under control. Then Khrushchev blinked and withdrew his weaponry from Cuba. I often wondered what would have happened to our country and the world if Khrushchev hadn't blinked.

Ripley's Believe It or Not

The last year of our clinical experience was intense and often chaotic. There was a long list of procedures that we needed to master before we could graduate. I can remember checking this list and actively searching it for tasks not yet observed or completed.

Most of the third year was spent on the Medical-Surgical floors. We were given assignments as if we already graduated as registered professional nurses. We became part of the nursing staff (unpaid staff!) on that floor.

One day, we might be assigned as the medication nurse, responsible for pouring all of the medications for around forty patients or more. Another day, we would be responsible for all patient dressing changes and other procedures as ordered by the attending physicians. The third assignment would be taking vital signs on all patients every four hours. It was a frantically busy time for senior students.

Shadowing the Head Nurse soon morphed into assisting her as our skills improved. I found the "doctor protocol" very interesting. Whenever a doctor came on the floor, all nurses had to stand. The Head Nurse would give the doctor a verbal report about his patient, making sure that all of the patient's blood work and other test reports were in the chart. She would then accompany him as he visited each patient.

Some of us were faced with challenging treatment assignments, but our instructors were always available for consulting, or we could look it up in our procedure manual. Even with all of these helpful tools, we made mistakes. No patient suffered but student nurses sure felt like idiots.

Sometimes we managed to make a procedure more difficult and costly than necessary. One student in our class mistakenly irrigated a colostomy opening with an intravenous solution of 5 percent glucose in water, using small intravenous tubing. It seemed to take forever for that costly fluid to go through! The instructor was actually too stunned to say anything for quite a while. When she got over her shock, she instructed the hapless student to get the correct (larger) rectal tubing and enema bag and use warm tap water mixed with a mild soap solution. A much cheaper solution!

Another student was instructed to take the vital signs of everyone in a fourteen-bed ward. She did exactly as instructed. Everybody in the ward got their blood pressure and pulse checked, both patients and their visitors were included. A fine example of following orders!

But the real winner of the "Believe it or Not" contest belongs to our classmate who confessed the following incident at our forty-fifth nursing class reunion.

This nursing tale of woe happened sometime after our graduation. She was Head Nurse on "Medical 3," working the night shift, when a patient died and the body had to be taken to the morgue. The funeral home staff had been notified and was on the way to pick up the body.

Suddenly, the electricity went out. The emergency generator came on but the elevators, of course, were not working. That meant a trip to the morgue down the stairs with a dead body! To the basement!

So, the Head Nurse and three staff members worked together to carry the body. Dim lighting in the stairwell and the weight of the body soon caused the unthinkable to happen. The person holding one of the legs lost her balance and she dropped her load. The sound was echoed over and over in the stairwell...*thump, thump, thump,* as the body descended, unaided, down the stairs, until the staff caught up to it. Stephen King would have been impressed with this scene.

On the last day of our clinical duty, two of my classmates forgot their patient (an elderly Mercy nun) in a Hoyer Lift. This was a sling-like device that transferred a patient from the bed to a chair. The poor sister was left to swing in the breeze, until found and assisted out of her Hoyer lift by a surprised staff nurse.

I'm sure that there are many more tales to be told, but my classmates have chosen to remain silent. You know who you are. In reality, everybody thought that everyone else knew what they were doing. In truth, nobody did, at least not all the time. No patient was seriously injured and some actually laughed along with us proving that laughter is truly the best medicine.

Nurse: Heal Thyself

A few classmates became patients themselves while at Mercy. One emergency room visitor was a student who had been invited to stay over at another student's home, where they had a great time drinking Cherry Berries, a very tasty alcoholic drink. The drink was so good that soon her feet got tangled up, causing her to fall and hit her chin.

But they had to get back to Marian Hall before the curfew. Her chin laceration would not stop bleeding no matter what nursing measures were tried. Arriving at the dorm, they attempted to sneak by the Housemother, but failed.

Of course, Sister Mary Ethel was called and the student was sent to the emergency room reeking of Cherry Berries. The intern on duty stitched up her chin, while avoiding inhaling, then sent her on her way.

Rachel, another student, had been sick for about two days. She had gone to see Sister Mary Claver who gave her some of her good drugs but these didn't seem to help her. On the third night, another student nurse came to her rescue. Mary Lee put her in a wheelchair and took her through the dripping dark tunnel to the emergency hospital, where Rachel got bigger and better drugs. Another fine example of Mercy Girls looking out for each other!

Talented Angels of Mercy

All work and no play makes for a dull Jane or a dull student nurse. The nuns decided that our senior class should put on a play to entertain our parents and younger nursing students. This was not the best timing as we were trying to cram in studies and clinical experiences for the last four months of school.

I don't know who decided to appoint Sara S. and me in charge of coming up with an entertainment idea for the evening. We put our heads together and came up with a variety-style show and asked our classmates to volunteer and display their many talents besides nursing. We extended this fun opportunity to the two other classes.

I became a bum named Areolie and Sara became a bum named Dolly. We teased our hair up to a high height and wore mismatched outfits of stripes, polka dots and plaids. We introduced the acts one by one, while sitting on the edge of the stage in the big conference hall.

No one had any idea that we had a ballerina in our class. She tiptoed all across the stage in her lovely tutu.

Kathy M. and Bonnie C. sang a song called "There's a Hole in the Bucket, Dear Henry!" They had been singing duets in the communal shower room since day one, but had a chance to have a larger number of people hear their beautiful voices that evening.

The Checkerboard Squares soon came out tap dancing across the stage, led by Louise S. and Diane E.. A group of ten students performed a very inventive routine of singing and dancing with colorful costumes. Another group of students did a routine from the musical *South Pacific*. They really washed someone's hair, while singing "I'm going to Wash that Man Right Out of My Hair."

Then there were the Suits. Their act was literally dressing in suits that had specific names, like a box suit was a suit worn by a student in a box. Sis M. demonstrated the walking suit by simply walking across the stage. Pat G. wore a suit that was covered with green ivy to model an "ivy league" suit.

The evening entertainment was a big hit. Our families and friends enjoyed all of the acts. Sister Mary Ethel graciously invited everyone to stay afterwards and enjoy some refreshments that she and the nuns had provided. We were lucky that Madge hadn't raided the kitchen the night before the play and purloined a good portion of the goodies for us to enjoy.

My First Job

After graduation, Emilie and I began searching for a job. We went to see the Director of Nurses at Mount St. Mary's Hospital in Niagara Falls, New York. She wasn't a Mercy nun and seemed quite nice. Emilie and I were hired and began working two weeks after graduating from Mercy Hospital School of Nursing.

I was a nervous new graduate on the first day of orientation at the hospital. I signed a lot of papers and noted that I would be earning approximately $5,000.00 a year, with time and a half for holidays. It wasn't much money; perhaps $2.40 per hour. I would have to live at home for a while until I could save some money to move out.

The amount of pay reminded me of what the Big E. told my mother and me when I applied for admission to the school. My profession was a calling from God, not for material gain. Well, my starting pay sure proved that nun right! I was living at home and, thankfully, my parents weren't charging me rent. I had no car and had to rely on public transportation or a ride into work with another nurse who lived down the street.

I started work and soon realized the scheduling nightmare that often happened to new nurses. Only one weekend off per month, and two days off in a row was rare. One day I would be working the second shift from three-thirty p.m. to eleven-thirty p.m., and then have to come in for a seven-thirty a.m. to three-thirty p.m. shift the next day. The patients thought that I had slept overnight in an empty patient bed. Such was the working life of a new graduate.

The Blessed Proposal

Mrs. C., the Head Nurse on my floor, was preparing the staff Christmas/New Year's holiday assignments, and asked everyone for their preferred requests. Naturally, everyone wanted Christmas Day off. I, of course, being a new staff member, was assigned to work Christmas Eve, three-thirty p.m. to eleven-thirty p.m. and then return on Christmas Day, seven-thirty a.m. to three-thirty p.m.

She must have really had me on her mind a lot, as she also kindly assigned me to work that shift on New Year's Eve and New Year's Day as well. Sister Mary Ethel's words, "a calling from God, dear..." leapt into my brain and a growl escaped from my lips.

Working that Christmas Eve, I noticed the ward was quieter than usual on the second shift and there were very few patients. The doctors had discharged most of their patients' home for the holiday.

My boyfriend Joe was meeting me for midnight mass in the hospital chapel, and I really wanted to finish my shift in time.

For once, I finished the patient charting and the narcotic count in record time. I gave the night nurse a quick patient report before I headed to the chapel for mass.

Joe, who was a senior at Niagara University that year, was seated close to the altar, waiting for me. Mass was beautifully celebrated with flowers and music.

At the end of Mass, Joe turned to me and opened a jewelry box that held a diamond ring.

"Maureen, will you marry me?" Joe asked in a hushed voice.

My mouth fell open and tears filled my eyes. Then I heard applause coming from the choir loft. Joe and I turned to see all the nuns looking down on us, smiling and applauding.

"Yes," I said to my future husband, and was bold enough to kiss him in front of God and the nuns. Well, I thought to myself, maybe working holidays has its advantages.

Section 4

Back To the Future

The 45th Nursing School Reunion

The greenery of a Western New York summer had morphed into blazing shades of red, orange, and yellow as the cooler days of October began. Thirty Mercy Girls attended the 45th Nursing School Reunion Dinner in 2008. It was so warm that year that a coat was not necessary—a sweater would do.

We were older, but still retained our old Mercy-selves somewhere deep inside. We met in a small hotel in downtown Niagara Falls. But the site didn't matter. We could have met in a bus shelter and the result would be the same: laughter and memories shared.

The world economy was in a free fall in 2008, due to a global financial crisis, and boomers were rethinking their retirement plans. America was strongly contemplating the election of a first-ever black President, reminding us all of the Kennedy years of the 60s when the first Catholic was elected as America's 35th president.

In the midst of all these topsy-turvy world events, we eagerly got together again…and reminisced, as we always did. We told old stories of nursing school days, days that became new again in the retelling. In our minds, we were back at Mercy, in the dorm, we were young again and full of hopes, plans, and dreams. As always at our reunions, we re-read Beaver's Bloopers, laughing and fondly remembering that dear, funny nun who had no idea how much she meant to the class of 1963.

Our 50th Reunion

In the summer of 2013, we will hold our 50th nursing school reunion. Most of us will be anxious to attend. Those that can't be there in person will be with us in spirit. We imagine the memories will come easily and delightfully to us. Beaver's Bloopers will ring out again, to peals of laughter. It will be a very special reunion for us all.

We treasure those years at Mercy, as do the other Mercy Girls. It was three years of ups and downs…and round and rounds…all told, it's been a fine journey.

Thank you, dear Mercy Girls, for being along for the trip. It's been totally delightful.

Career Paths

As we looked at the divergent career paths of our classmates, we were unable to find anyone who followed in the footsteps of Sister Mary Ethel as a Director of a Nursing School. Moe and Mary wondered why Mumme had never considered that option. Certainly, she had spent the most time with Sister during training.

However, we know now that many of us have echoed our beloved Beaver. We have found that over time, we managed to produce our own share of bloopers as nurses and teachers. We are always on the lookout to make sure no one is writing them down. Some of us are suspicious, if we are out for dinner, and Mumme takes out a pen and with twinkling eyes and a mischievous grin, begins to write feverishly on the nearest piece of paper, which might be the menu.

We no longer laugh at our dear Sister Beaver, but we have come to understand her. We appreciate that in her wisdom, she realized that anxious student nurses need humor and if they suppressed it, they might end up visiting her at the health office.

We recall reading some wonderful memoirs and wondering: *Whatever happened to the author after the book was written, and what happened to the people that trotted alongside in those pages?* If you like a book a lot, you don't ever want to leave the author's world; you always seek more: an epilogue, an afterward, a post-note, why even a bibliography will do in a pinch.

Well, here is our Mercy Girls epilogue-world; here is what happened to us afterwards:

> Some of us stayed with a nursing career, some not. Some worked full time, some worked part time, and some never worked after graduation.

> Most married, had children; some did not.

> Some of us moved away from the Buffalo area; one left the country (guess who).

The nurses-who-nursed chose a wide variety of nursing careers and specialties:

> Coronary care; long term care, obstetrics, pediatrics, oncology, public health, mental health, home care, physician's offices, and nurse practitioners. Some became managers, directors, and CEOs.

> A few are still working, most are retired, and, of course, some of us are dead but always remembered and missed by the living.

A few of us became authors. At our 50th reunion, three authors will make a small speech...it will go like this... "Sometimes there is a story to be told..."

Appendix A

History: Mercy Hospital School of Nursing
(We knew you'd want to read this!)

The Mercy Hospital School of Nursing (1904–1967) opened its doors in 1904, in Buffalo, New York, when the Sisters of Mercy religious community saw a need to meet the community's health needs. The school issued its first annual report in December 1905 by saying, "No sooner was the hospital opened than a group of young women formed the nucleus of the personal department. Lectures are given by members of the hospital staff."

The school graduated two students in 1906, but seventy-five more women graduated between then and 1926.

The locations of the school varied until the four-story residence, Marian Hall was built on Choate Avenue, adjacent to Mercy Hospital of South Buffalo on Abbott Road. A total of 1,362 women received their Registered Nurse degree from the school.

Throughout its existence, the school had affiliations with the New York Foundling Hospital in New York City, the Buffalo Psychiatric Center, the Rochester State Hospital, the Gowanda State Hospital, the Children's Hospital of Buffalo, the J. N. Adam Memorial Hospital of Perrysburg, New York for Tuberculosis Nursing and St. Vincent's Hospital for Psychiatric Nursing in Westchester County, Harrison, New York.

These 1,362 graduate nurses began their careers in numerous hospitals, countries, schools, the armed forces, doctors' offices and the public health departments. Some of the graduates continued their educations in nursing by receiving bachelors and masters degrees after leaving the three-year program.

In 1966, there were more than 700 hospital-based nursing programs in the United States; the dominant educational pattern for nursing education until the end of the 1970s. Thereafter, associate degree (two year) and baccalaureate degree (four year) nursing programs became the preferred entry point for the nursing profession. As a result, after a sixty-three year existence, Mercy Hospital School of Nursing closed its doors to the three-year program in 1967.

In 1982, the number of hospital-based schools had decreased to less than 300; and by 2004, there were only sixty-eight diploma nursing programs remaining in the country. Sadly, Mercy Hospital School of Nursing was not one of them.

Today, Trocaire College, located in Marian Hall, is a vibrant, multi-dimensional Catholic college, and continues to offer nursing and other degree programs in the spirit of the Sisters of Mercy.

Appendix B

Beaver's Bloopers (Inane Utterances)
(We just knew you'd appreciate these words of nursing wisdom!)

Sister Mary Claver, A.K.A, The Beaver, Author (October 25, 1961 to June 8, 1962)

I'd like to ask you one or two thoughts.

We, as nurses, should be aware of toys—especially now that everyone is talking about it.

And with a child—we usually mummify the patient.

What are you enjoying up there so much, Miss I?

You just stay here, Miss Winterbottom—you're it—aren't you happy?

You all set—or are you entertaining up there?

We can be sure—our doctors—our men...

And I learnt it the other day...

Some of you may say...why all the sterility?

Miss Winter mint...err...mantel...

I predict...and I wish I had a patient.

I'm coughing—and talking—and sneezing—and spraying.

If you are going to be attentive to a patient—make it a patient with feelings!

I think she's a coward if she doesn't...and that's pretty strong feelings!

The last thing to do with a patient's clothes is to roll 'em up in newspaper and stick them in the closet 'til someone calls for them.

Sit up there! Deceive me if you will!

My goodness! Even Miss Bedford's arm is off this morning!

I time the length of stay of my sterile dishes...

If this patient can assist me to get on this bedpan...

Now my sleeves are up to your elbow and I'm ready for ACTION!

You'd look like an Icelander too!

I wash my hands cause I'm liable to put my contaminated hands up around your mask or hairline.

Things move around here...I thought I had one...Hrmppp!

I have a square—and I use it!

Want to look out there, Miss-you-Winter–mint?

And at that time, you can tie the visitor up.

In addition to this, now we should have a tongue.

You'll find most patients with throat conditions breathe.

The patient nods his head and you pinch it off.

Sometimes a person could live right down the street and you could still get your medications mixed up.

We're not anxious for you to make...

Let us now pray for the relatives of students who are ill.

I asked Miss-ah–some person...to put these into...Oh! Will you wait just one moment!

Girls, be very observant and watch, and you too can get into the medicine!

The narcotics key is on a separate key.

Syringes and needles are on the floor.

All right now! Attention now! Never mind for a moment!

Some doctors do...cause they don't have anyone to sterilize.

If you learn to cup your hand as I'm doing, you won't have an accident.

In the beginning, you're going to have a lot of thumbs.

Spread the dossil around in a circular motor...

I've been around a few eras.

We were all just gasping when he made his...

And those of you who have a book...and I didn't, which I don't.

And you're thinking of...right?

To give an IM shot in the buttocks, bring their pajama tops down.

Girls, when you draw the line on the buttocks, you're not making a blessing!

You can never give a hypodermic that's not well.

We have a child coming in who's swallowed...

Some of these patients may not hear you say, "Open your tongue!"

The doctor will give you a sign, "Halt!" into the stomach.

It's easy for you...you don't have to look for someone to mop up!

Rectal tube inserted...more comfortable flatus removed.

Get in! Get out! And distract the patient!

He weighed 200 pounds! I didn't think he'd faint! The bigger they are, the more they fall over.

Most of these rectal patients have rectal drainage.

Don't put hot water into the chair...take its temperature.

If you have a large cut hand...

Don't have this balloon too ballooned.

There are caps in front...cog them down.

You can put on their call light and go back in.

In a few weeks, you will be taking drugs.

Lock your medicine chest and GO!

It's rather disorderly to have all the medication on the outside of the bottle.

The ID band is the best way...and also check on the floor.

Because the patient would often use the soufflé cup as an ashtray...

People whose teeth have been deceived by enamel...

Patients who take bathtubs...err...tub baths.

Do you see what I mean? Well then, stand!

My, your dress is baggy, Miss O'Neill!

Be out of bed with a many-tailed binder.

Never go into a patient's skin, cause the patient might not want you around the next day.

Elasticized stockings have become very popular with our own doctors.

Be sure the side rails are up, and let the person come to the door who wants you or needs you.

Of course this may be due to they don't have time to get into a box.

Sometimes they get so excited if something's needed...an urn.

They won't have fared well if they come into YOUR assistance!

I, myself, would like to get a small graduate!

You can give all kinds of gas, but it won't do any good unless the patient breathes it in!

Maybe you gave this patient a bath and his skin was quite white. Now it's blue. This indicates that some thing's wrong!

Usually there are telling tales. We often fill this with water so that in between if there is any mucous around...is that clear?

When you are watching these patients, you can do only one thing...watch them. I say this not to be an alarmist.

Very often the doctor on these patients...

I'll pinch this off or else the water would go into Mrs. Bedford and I'd be the rest of the day getting it out.

Be sure there is not a weight around their neck.

The returns will be mucous or a clock.

Any doctor I've ever seen who's put in a tube...

Open your eyes! See and observe!

If you sit on a tube...or put a big heavy arm or leg on a tube...or a buttock...

If a patient sits on a tube, he'll say, "Some thing's wrong, Nurse," and it behooves you to get busy!

After this tube is attached to your wagon...

Miss-ah-Zabook there!

You people in the front there are too far away!

He grew up into adulthood and was fed directly into the stomach wall.

She came to Mercy to die!

Now get ready for death, cause anything's possible with the grace of God!

It usually adheres to or clings to the tube...so usually you do...as I do...I did.

You'll notice on this sheet of Wagenstein suction...

The patient who has a set up...

The way it's done is, Father gets on the floor.

Here's my rectal area...what's so funny up there, Miss Paltry...uh Pantry?

If you break this syringe, it's a couple of dollars...but a 50cc syringe is $8 or $9...so my advice is to use this one.

We don't leave the emesis basin around and have the ferns and flowers falling into it.

In irrigations of our hospital, we use clean equipment.

There are signs here: "Please do not disturb Nurse!"

Author's Note: After a long, dedicated nursing education career, Sister Mary Claver (our beloved "Beaver") died in 1998. She was eighty-nine years old. We miss her still.